CARL FISCHER ORIGINAL METHODS

download at
carlfischer.com

Jean Baptiste

Arban

Complete Conservatory Method for Trumpet/Cornet

or

E♭ Alto, B♭ Tenor, E♭ Baritone Saxophones
Euphonium and B♭ Bass Tuba
in Treble Clef

Edited by
Thomas Hooten and Jennifer Marotta

Contains:

Arban's Original and Complete Method

The Art of Phrasing (150 Songs and Operatic Airs)

68 Duets for Two Cornets

14 Characteristic Studies

12 Celebrated Fantaisies and Airs Variés

CARL FISCHER®

O21X

ISBN 978-0-8258-9314-8

Table of Contents

Notes and Track Listings for the MP3 Accompaniment Audio

12 Celebrated Fantaisies and Airs Variés

Credits
Pianist: John Walker
Recording Engineer: Dietr Poppen
Supervising Engineer: Joseph Firman
Recorded on the Fazioli concert grand piano in the Performing Arts Center, Brookings, SD

Acknowledgements

Dr. Alan Taylor, professor of high brass at South Dakota State University for his in-depth knowledge of Arban's tempos and style tradition, and road-testing of the finished product.

Dr. Michael Reger and the administration of South Dakota State University for his in-depth knowledge of Arban's tempos and style tradition, and road-testing of the finished product.

Dr. Michael Reger and the administration of South Dakota State University for use of the recording facility.

Using This Recording

I hope you will find these accompaniments helpful in practice, but since there are so many pauses because of cadenzas, they are not ideal for use in live performance. Each fantasy is recorded on several tracks so that you may jump back and forth between variations, or program the player to play one variation over and over. Each track is introduced by metronome clicks, unless the accompaniment itself leads you in. Tempos are moderate, and occasionally flexible according to traditional interpretations. Breaths are taken in the accompaniment where needed.

The cadenzas pose a minor problem with a play-along recording such as this. Generally, I have continued the tracks through short cadenzas, and stopped the tracks for the longer ones. You should play through the short cadenzas and try to meet up with the piano at the end. For longer cadenzas, hit the stop button, play the cadenza, then start the next track. There will be clicks to lead into the next section. In a few instances the track will continue in silence through the cadenza, then give re-enter clicks at the end (Fantasy No. 6). There are also a few cadenzas where accompanying chords that occur in the middle or end are omitted (for example, No. 1, after the first long cadenza). It is just not worth the trouble trying to play through a long stretch of silence and find a chord at the end of it.

According to traditional band performances, the interludes between variations were usually played quite fast, and were unrelated in tempo to the surrounding variations. That style is adopted here with no qualms. Every fantasy also traditionally ends with an accelerando, notated or not, which is also done here.

The Fantasy and Variations on *Actéon* (No. 2) is rarely played because it is written for the A-cornet and Air Varié on a Folk Song (No. 7) contains many extended cadenzas and, therefore, this piece has been eliminated from the audio.

—John Walker, 2005

Arban's Fantasies Accompaniment Audio MP3s

No. 1: Fantaisie and Variations on a Cavatina from *Beatrice di Tenda* by Vincenzo Bellini
Track 01 Introduction-Andante
Track 02 Theme
Track 03 Variation 1
Track 04 Variation 2
Track 05 Variation 3 and Finale I
Track 06 Finale II

No. 3: Fantaisie Brillante
Track 07 Introduction-Allegro maestoso
Track 08 Interlude
Track 09 Theme
Track 10 Variation 1
Track 11 Variation 2
Track 12 Variation 3

No. 4: Variations on a Tyrolean Song
Track 13 Introduction-Andante moderato
Track 14 Theme-Andante
Track 15 Variation 1
Track 16 Variation 2
Track 17 Variation 3
Track 18 Variation 4
Track 19 Rondo-Allegro

No. 5: Variations on a song *The Beautiful Snow*
Track 20 Andante quasi Allegretto
Track 21 Variation 1
Track 22 Variation 2
Track 23 Variation 3
Track 24 Finale-Lento
Track 25 Allegro

No. 6: Cavatina and Variations
Track 26 Andante
Track 27 Andante, continued
Track 28 Theme-Moderato
Track 29 Variation 1
Track 30 Variation 2
Track 31 Variation 3

No. 8: Caprice and Variations
Track 32 Andantino
Track 33 Andante moderato
Track 34 Variation 1 – Allegro moderato
Track 35 Variation 2
Track 36 Variation 3- Piu lento

No. 9: Fantaisie and Variations on a German Theme
Track 37 Allegro moderato
Track 38 Interlude
Track 39 Theme0Andante
Track 40 Variation 1
Track 41 Variation 2
Track 42 Variation 3
Track 43 Finale

No. 10: Variations on a Theme by Carl Maria Weber
Track 44 Introduction-Allegro moderato
Track 45 Interlude
Track 46 Theme-Andantino
Track 47 Variation 1
Track 48 Variation 2
Track 49 Variation 3
Track 50 Variation 4

No. 11: Fantaisie and Variations on *The Carnival of Venice*
Track 51 Introduction-Allegretto
Track 52 Interlude, Theme
Track 53 Interlude, Variation 1
Track 54 Interlude, Variation 2
Track 55 Interlude, Variation 3- Andante
Track 56 Interlude, Variation 4

No. 12: Variations on a theme from *Norma* by Vincenzo Bellini
Track 57 Andante Maestoso
Track 58 Interlude
Track 59 Theme-moderato
Track 60 Variation 1
Track 61 Variation 2
Track 62 Più lento

14 Characteristic Studies

Credits
Trumpet: Thomas Hooten
Recording Engineer: Sonny Ausman
Producer: Jeniifer Marotta

Using This Recording

Audio files of the 14 *Characteristic Studies* have been added to this newly revised edition. Performed by the editor himself, these recordings serve as an introductory model for students who are just beginning to learn these time-tested etudes. The interpretations should not be considered absolute, but rather as an example to help facilitate the learning process and introduce the concepts behind the music.

These studies have become the standard for trumpeters to showcase their diligent progress within the method. They will no doubt test strength and endurance. With careful study and dedication alongside keen listening to the recordings, the student will be able to successfully master the challenges presented.

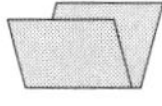

Arban's Characteristic Studies Audio MP3s

Track 01 Characteristic Study No. 1
Track 02 Characteristic Study No. 2
Track 03 Characteristic Study No. 3
Track 04 Characteristic Study No. 4
Track 05 Characteristic Study No. 5
Track 06 Characteristic Study No. 6
Track 07 Characteristic Study No. 7
Track 08 Characteristic Study No. 8
Track 09 Characteristic Study No. 9
Track 10 Characteristic Study No. 10
Track 11 Characteristic Study No. 11
Track 12 Characteristic Study No. 12
Track 13 Characteristic Study No. 13
Track 14 Characteristic Study No. 14

Fingering Chart for Trumpet/Cornet

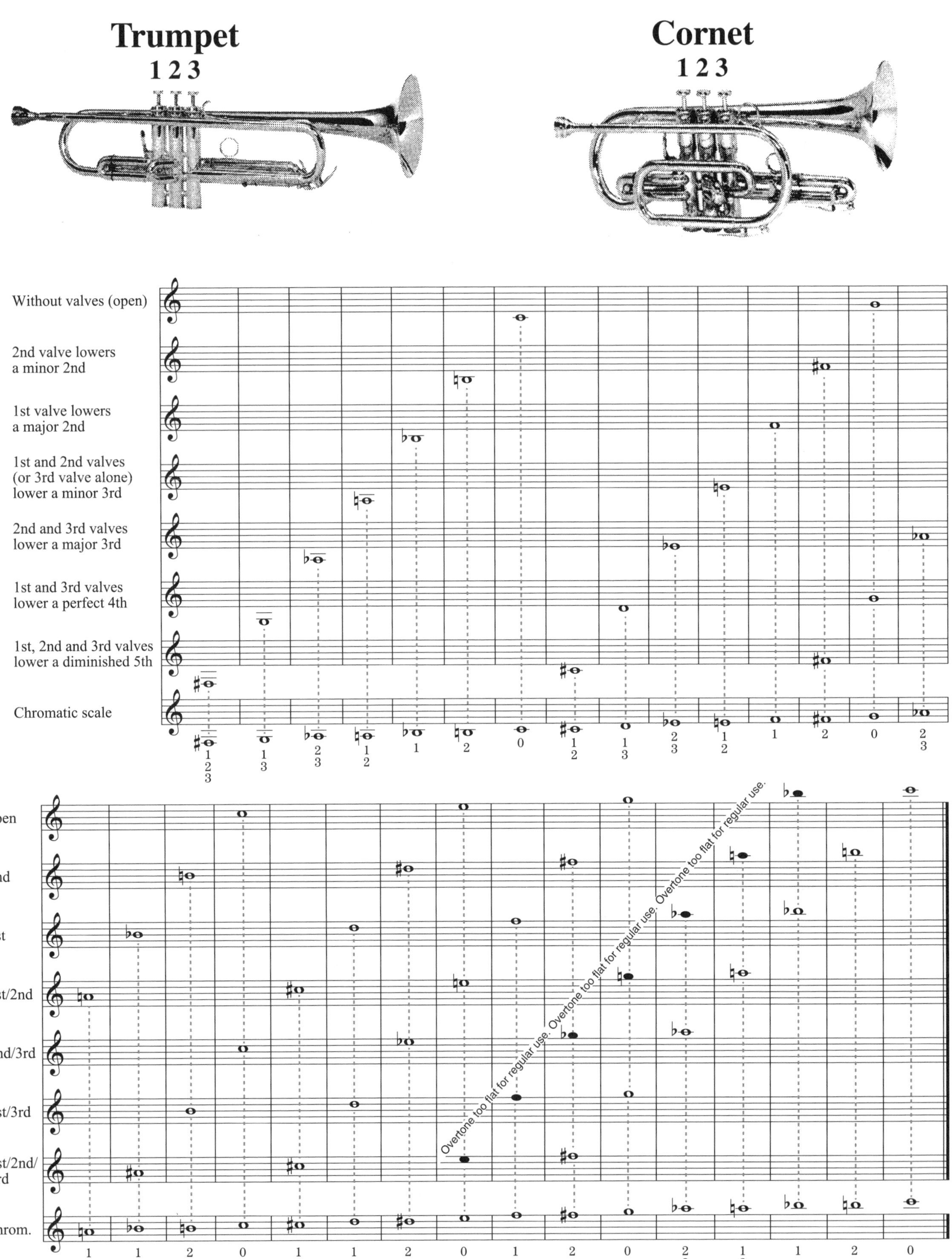

Diagram of the Trumpet and Cornet

Trumpet

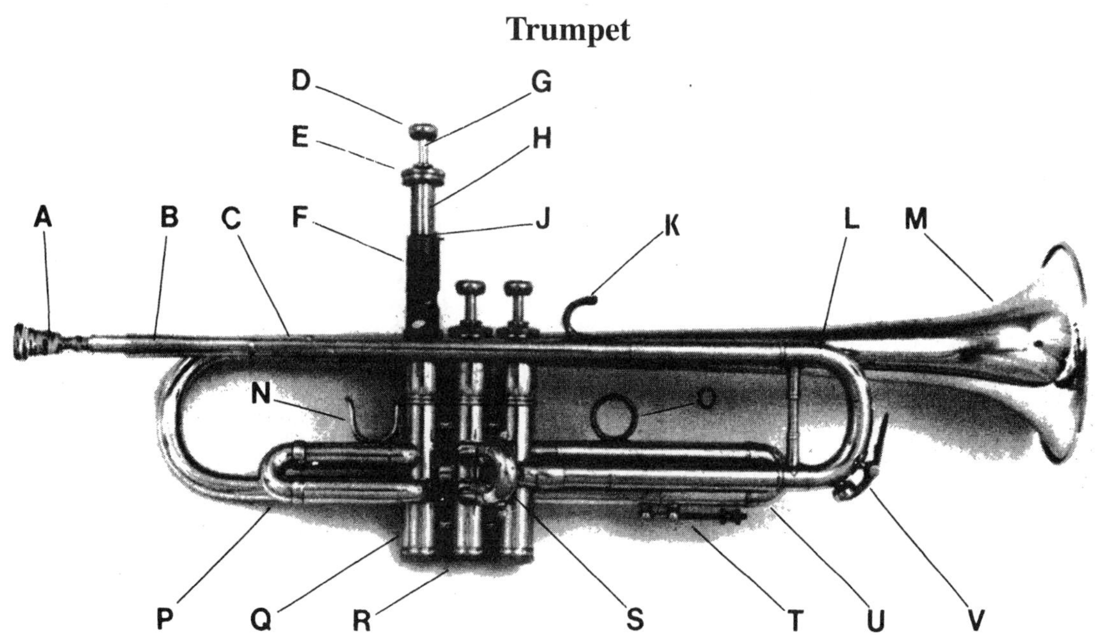

A - Mouthpiece
B - Mouthpiece receiver
C - Leadpipe
D - Finger button
E - Valve cap-top
F - Piston
G - Piston stem

H - Spring barrel
J - Piston guide
K - Finger hook
L - Main tuning slide
M - Bell
N - Thumb throw
O - Finger ring

P - 1st Valve tuning slide
Q - Valve casing
R - Valve cap-bottom
S - 2nd Valve tuning slide
T - Adjustable slide stop
U - 3rd Valve tuning slide
V - Water key

Cornet

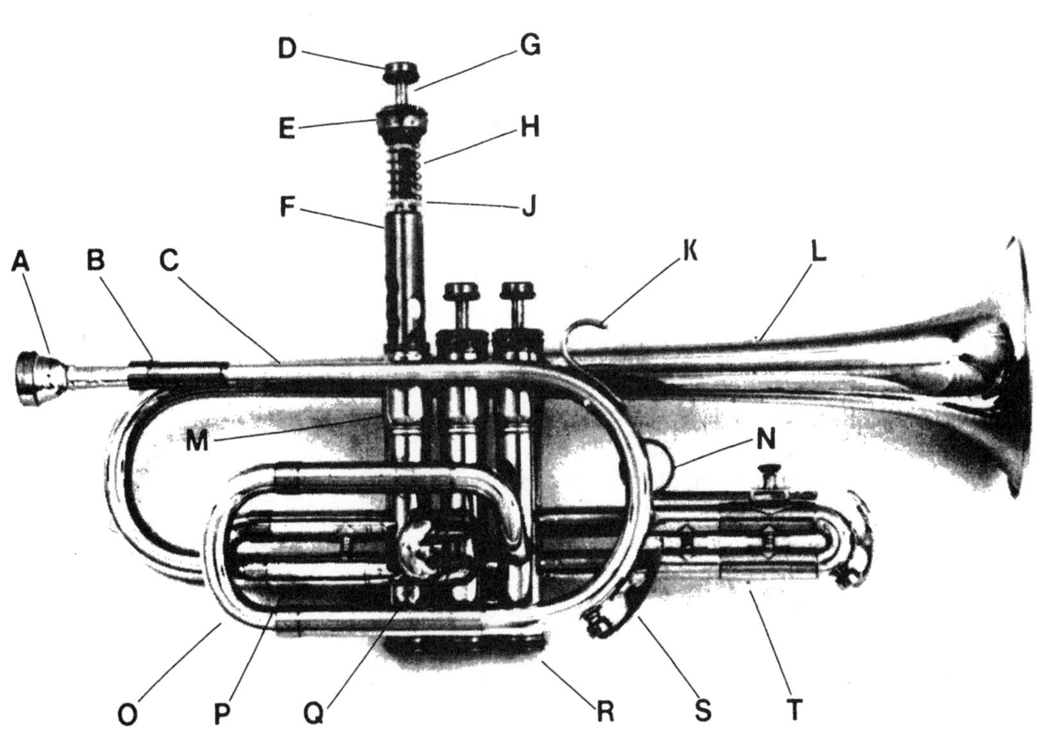

A - Mouthpiece
B - Mouthpiece receiver
C - Leadpipe
D - Finger button
E - Valve cap-top
F - Piston
G - Piston stem

H - Valve spring
J - Piston guide
K - Finger hook
L - Bell
M - Valve casing
N - Adjustable finger ring
O - Main tuning slide

P - 1st Valve tuning slide
Q - 2nd Valve tuning slide
R - Valve cap-bottom
S - Water key
T - 3rd Valve tuning slide

Preface to the 1894 and 1936 Editions

It may appear somewhat strange to undertake the defense of the cornet at a time when this instrument has given proof of its excellence, both in the orchestra and in solo performance, where it is no less indispensable to the composer, and no less liked by the public than the flute, the clarinet, and even the violin; where, in short, it has definitely won for itself the elevated position to which the beauty of its tone, the perfection of its mechanism and the immensity of its resources, so justly entitle it.

But this was not always the case; the cornet was far less successful when it first appeared; and, indeed, not many years ago, the masses treated the instrument with supreme indifference, while that time-honored antagonist—routine—contested its qualities, and strove hard to prohibit their application. This phenomenon, however, is of never-failing recurrence at the birth of every new invention, however excellent it may be, and of this fact the appearance of the saxhorn and the saxophone, instruments of still more recent date than the cornet, gave a new and striking proof.

The first musicians who played the cornet were, for the most part, either horn or trumpet players. Each imparted to his performance the peculiarities resulting from his tastes, his abilities and his habits, and I need scarcely add that the kind of performance which resulted from so many incomplete and heterogeneous elements was deficient in the extreme, and, for a long while, presented the lamentable spectacle of imperfections and failures of the most painful description.

Gradually, however, matters assumed a more favorable aspect. Performers really worthy of the name of artists began to make their appearance. However, regardless of the brilliant accomplishments of such performers, they could not deny the faults of their original training, viz., the total lack of qualifications necessary for ensemble playing, and decided musicianly tendencies. Some excited admiration for their extreme agility; others were applauded for the expression with which they played; one was remarkable for lip; another for the high tone to which he ascended; others for the brilliancy and volume of their tone. In my opinion, it was the reign of specialists, but it does not appear that a single one of the players then in vogue ever thought of realizing or of obtaining the sum total of qualities which alone can constitute a great artist.

This, then, is the point upon which I wish to insist, and to which I wish to call particular attention. At the present time, the incompleteness of the old school of performers is unanimously acknowledged, as is also the insufficiency of their instruction. That which is required is methodical execution and methodical instruction. It is not sufficient to phrase well or to execute difficult passages with skill. It is necessary that both these things should be equally well done. In a word, it is necessary that the cornet, as well as the flute, the clarinet, the violin, and the voice, should possess the pure style and the grand method of which a few professors, the Conservatory in particular, have conserved the precious secret and the salutary traditions.

This is the aim which I have incessantly kept in view throughout my long career; and if a numerous series of brilliant successes obtained in the presence of the most competent judges and the most critical audiences, give me the right to believe that I have, at any rate, approached the desired end, I shall not be laying myself open to the charge of presumption, in confidently entering upon the delicate mission of transmitting to others the results of my own thorough studies and assiduous practice.[1] I have long been a professor, and this work is to a certain extent merely the résumé of a long experience which each day has brought nearer to perfection.

My explanations will be found as short and clear as possible, for I wish to instruct and not to terrify the student. Long pages of "text" are not always read, and it is highly advantageous to replace the latter by exercises and examples. This is the wealth which I consider cannot be too lavishly accumulated; this is the source which can never be too plentifully drawn from. This, however, will be perceived from the extent of the present volume, in which, in my opinion, will be found the solution of all difficulties and of all problems.

I have endeavored throughout to compose studies of a melodic nature, and in general to render the study of instrument as agreeable as possible. In a word, I have endeavored to lead the pupil, without discouragement, to the highest limits of execution, sentiment and style, destined to characterize the new school.

—Jean Baptiste Arban

1 The results which I have obtained in France, Germany and England victoriously plead the cause of the cornet, and prove that the latter can compete with the most popular of instruments. In a concert given by the "Societe des Concerts du Conservatoire" in 1848, I played the famous air for the flute composed by Boehme on a Swiss theme, comprising, as is well known, an intentional combination of enormous difficulties. From that day forth I may say the cornet took its place among classic instruments. In the piece of music just alluded to, I performed the flute tonguing in double staccato, also the triple staccato, which I am the first to have applied to the cornet.

Editors' Note

Jean Baptiste Arban's *Complete Conservatory Method for trumpet* has remained the most widely used and comprehensive method book for trumpet. Our intention in this new edition is to clarify and update Arban's book for modern times, not to change his content. It is important to read Arban's text throughout the book. With the use of footnotes, we have clarified some of his insights, while including up-to-date techniques and practices that have changed since the 1982 edition.

In addition to significant advancements in the quality of trumpets since Arban's time, there have also been advancements in the understanding of how one becomes proficient at certain skills. In order to get the most benefit out of Arban's method book, one must be efficient with their practice habits. To be successful as a professional musician, we must first learn what it is to be a professional student. The skills and abilities that are needed to be successful in music are learned and practiced for countless hours throughout the performer's entire career. Although each person has their own strengths, we all have to put in the time and dedication to work on our weaknesses in order to become well-rounded in our abilities. In doing this, one may be able to share their musical message without technical limitations.

Building a solid foundation as a musician begins with listening. This may include ear training, singing, listening to recordings, recording yourself, taking lessons, and going to live performances. No matter how advanced today's instruments are or how proficient our physical abilities become, you cannot replace good musicianship with good technique. The performer must have a very strong sound model in their head so that they are able to strive daily toward that model. The main goal is always making music with a good sound. If technical issues arise that inhibit this main goal, then those techniques must be addressed daily in order to continue to stay on the correct musical path.

Becoming proficient at your instrument takes time and dedication. We discourage the student from blindly diving into playing too much without a plan and common sense. The use of long-term and short-term goals helps to provide guidance in the practice room. In each session, the professional student should take frequent playing breaks, so that the embouchure and the mind have a chance to recover and to refocus, which will help to move toward the highest quality possible. It is very easy to over-play, which can lead to bad form and injury. Once a player is practicing with bad form, then bad habits are created. Playing the trumpet with bad form usually leads to a slow improvement curve, or even regression in progress. Several thirty-minute practice sessions are a good place to start. However, even within these thirty minutes, small breaks are needed. When taking a break from physically playing in each session, the student can also use the time for listening, working on fingerings, ear training, or many other engaging practice techniques that don't necessarily require one to be constantly playing. We recommend keeping a practice journal. A simple notebook that keeps track of your progress and what you are working on will help your practice sessions to have more clarity and purpose.

Use this simple formula when practicing:

1) Strive for small improvements. All big improvements come from a combination of little successes.
2) Use the best form that you can. This includes posture, the breath, removing excess tension, and the balance between using the air and embouchure efficiently.
3) Develop a consistent approach or routine that will help you to notice if you are moving in the right direction.

Arban's method has a vast array of exercises that are invaluable in each student's daily practice when used in accordance with your own personal goals. Try to refrain from blindly playing through the method; use specific exercises to help you to achieve your own personal daily and long term goals. Today, the trumpet player is required to do many things that are different than they were in Arban's era. Use this book in ways that aren't necessarily shown on each page: incorporate transposition, change the style if you are more jazz focused, or use different instruments (piccolo trumpet, Eb trumpet, flugelhorn, etc) for further study.

In your journey of improvement, you will encounter a number of successes and failures; these failures are your opportunity to learn and grow. However, if too much of your performance environment is requiring you to play in a forced or inefficient way, you must work toward altering your environment so that you are able to incorporate good habits in order to allow long term improvement. Use common sense when putting yourself into a challenging situation or opportunity. Coach John Wooden said, "If you don't have time to do it right, when will you have time to do it over again?"

While we all strive to improve to be the best musicians that we can, the ultimate goal is connecting with others through music, whether it be with the audience or the other performers. This connection is what makes music special, and we should never lose sight of that.

We would like to thank Vincent DiMartino and John Hagstrom for their invaluable insight into many of Arban's teachings, which helped greatly in this edition. We hope that this new edition will be easier to use and more beneficial to you in your journey as a brass player.

—Thomas Hooten and Jennifer Marotta

About Jean Baptiste Arban

Joseph Jean Baptiste Laurent Arban was born at Lyons, France, February 28, 1825. He entered the Conservatory at an early age, taking up the study of the trumpet under François Dauverné, and won first prize in 1845. His military term was spent in navy on board the "La Belle Poule," whose chief musician, Paulus, became Chief Musician of the *Garde a Paris* during the reign of Napoleon III.

After having been professor of saxhorn at the Military School (1857), Arban was elected professor of cornet at the Conservatory in 1869. After attending to these duties for a period of five years, he left the Conservatory for six years, returning again in 1880.

He was the most brilliant cornet player of his time, and his astonishing performance and triumphant concert tours throughout Europe were the means of establishing the valve cornet as one of the most popular of all musical instruments. Arban's artistic ideals, sound musicianship and invaluable instructive principles were perpetuated in his splendid *Method for the Cornet*, which has succeeded in maintaining the very highest position among similar instructive works and which has never been surpassed in point of practical superiority or artistic plan.

Arban died at Paris on April 9, 1889. He was an officer of the Académie, Knight of the Order of Leopold of Belgium, of Christ of Portugal, of Isabella the Catholic, and of the Cross of Russia.

About Thomas Hooten

Tom Hooten, Principal Trumpet of the Los Angeles Philharmonic, was born and raised in Tampa, Florida. He began his formal musical training at the University of South Florida, where he received his Bachelor of Music, then continued studies at Rice University where he earned his Master of Music. His primary trumpet teachers have included Armando Ghitalla, John Hagstrom, and Don Owen.

In 2000, Mr. Hooten earned a trumpet/cornet position with "The President's Own" United States Marine Band in Washington, D.C., where he was often a featured soloist. While living in the D.C area, Thomas was active in chamber and orchestral music, performing with groups such as the National Symphony Orchestra, Harrisburg Symphony, Washington Symphonic Brass, Arlington Symphony, and Baltimore Symphony.

Following his four-year enlistment in the Marine Band, Thomas was Assistant Principal Trumpet with the Indianapolis Symphony from 2004–2006, Principal Trumpet in the Atlanta Symphony from 2006–2012, and Principal Trumpet with the Los Angeles Philharmonic in 2012, where he is currently.

Thomas taught at Kennesaw State University from 2006–2012, is a committed educator, and actively performs as a soloist around the world. He can be heard on numerous Atlanta Symphony and Los Angeles Philharmonic recordings, as well as on his solo album, *Trumpet Call*.

About Jennifer Marotta

Jennifer Marotta, currently a freelance musician and trumpet teacher in Los Angeles, California, was raised in Naperville, IL. Marotta was a member of the "President's Own" United States Marine Band from 2001–2004, where she was an active soloist and chamber musician. Prior to the Marine Band, she earned her B.M. from Northwestern University and her M.M. from DePaul University, where her primary teachers were Barbara Butler and John Hagstrom.

Jennifer is currently a member of the Grand Teton Music Festival and the Chicago Music of the Baroque. She has also performed with the San Francisco Symphony, Atlanta Symphony Orchestra, Atlanta Opera, Indianapolis Symphony Orchestra, Greenville Symphony, Annapolis Symphony, and the New World Symphony.

Jennifer is co-editor for the International Women's Brass Conference's newsletter. She teaches trumpet students of all ages and levels, but specializes in helping young students to establish a strong fundamental base. Ms. Marotta acted as a visiting professor at Illinois State University in 2006, was Artist in Residence at Emory University from 2006–2010, and was the Assistant Professor of Trumpet at Kennesaw State University from 2006–2012.

Introduction
by Jean Baptiste Arban

Range

As indicated in the accompanying fingering chart, instruments with three valves have a chromatic range of two-and-a-half octaves, which, in the case of the cornet, extends from F♯ below the staff to C above the staff. Not every player however, succeeds in mastering this range with clearness and facility.[1] Therefore, when writing for these instruments, even if it is for a solo, it is advisable not to use the extreme limits of the scale shown in the chart. As a rule, the higher registers of the instruments are used much too frequently by arrangers and composers, which results in the performer losing the beautiful and characteristic tonal qualities peculiar to his instrument. It also leads to failure to properly perform the simplest passages, even when written in the middle register. To avoid this shortcoming, it is necessary to continually practice the instrument throughout its *entire* register, and to pay special attention to the chapter devoted to the study of the various intervals.[2]

The easiest portion of the cornet's range begins at low C and ends at G above the staff. One may easily ascend as high as B♭, but the B♮ and the C ought to be made use of very sparingly.[3] Regarding notes below C:[4]

These do not present any very great difficulties, although some players experience considerable trouble in producing them with clearness and sonority. However, they are very beautiful and effective when properly produced.

Alternate Fingering

The following suggestions are offered for producing F♮ below the staff and at the same time for facilitating certain passages, which are almost impossible with the fingering indicated in the first chart. In order to achieve this, the slide of the third valve should be drawn out a half step, in order to obtain a length of a major third instead of the usual minor third. In doing this, it will be advisable to adopt the following fingering, which is very popular among German cavalry trumpeters:[5]

In order that the F♮ may be produced in perfect tune, the tuning slide should be drawn out a little.[6]

Only in exceptional cases should one resort to devices such as this. I have only called attention to them here in order to acquaint the student with all the resources of the instrument.

Mouthpiece Position

The mouthpiece should be placed in the middle of the lips, two-thirds on the lower lip, and one-third on the upper lip. At any rate, this is the position which I have adopted, and which I believe to be the best.[7]

Players of the horn generally place the mouthpiece two-thirds on the upper lip and one-third on the lower, which is precisely the reverse of what I have just recommended for the cornet; but it might not be forgotten that great difference exists in the formation of this instrument as well as in the method of holding it, and that which may admirably suit the horn is unsatisfactory when applied to the cornet. What, after all, is the principal object as regards the position of the cornet? It should be perfectly horizontal. Accordingly, if the mouthpiece were placed as though the performer were playing the horn, the instrument would be in a falling position, resembling that of the clarinet.

Some teachers make a point of changing the position of the mouthpiece previously adopted by the pupils who apply to them. I have seldom known this method to succeed. To my own knowledge, several players, already possessed of

1 This may be true. However, this two-and-a-half octave range is the minimum required for all professional trumpet players today. (Hooten/Marotta)

2 Since Arban's time, the equipment and physical approach to the trumpet has progressed significantly. One is able to play more efficiently for longer periods of time in the upper register. While one must practice the full extent of the range daily, they also must be careful not to overdo it. (Hooten/Marotta)

3 Depending on the level of trumpeter, it is possible to play from pedal C to an octave above the high C that Arban describes. The full extent of this range takes years of practice to achieve, and the extremes should only be approached while maintaining good form. (Hooten/Marotta)

4 Pedal tones are not only used as a tool for improving one's playing, but they have also become more common within compositions in both solo and orchestral literature. Practice note: Stay focused in the aperture when playing below C and into the pedals. This is not the place to introduce a passive approach. For further studies with pedal tones, use James Stamp's *Warm-ups and Studies.* (Hooten/Marotta)

5 This fingering method is no longer common practice. Arban's alternate fingerings may be used if the player needs to access the low F in a place where quick third slide extension is not possible. (Hooten/Marotta)

6 Modern day trumpets are now built with a long enough third slide that the low F is possible to play in tune without having to adjust the tuning slide. (Hooten/Marotta)

7 Many players today play with this positioning, while there are others that play with a slight variation. It's important that the player avoids placing the top of the mouthpiece in the "red" of the upper lip, and that the placement is centered. There should be even pressure on the top and bottom. (Hooten/Marotta)

remarkable talent, have attempted what we call the "orthopedic system," which consists in correcting the wrong placing of the mouthpiece. I consider it my duty to say that these artists, after having wasted several years in uselessly trying the system in question, were compelled to return to their original placement of the mouthpiece, not one of them having obtained any advantage, while some of them were no longer able to play at all.

From all this I consider that when a player has commenced his studies faultily, he must, of course, try to improve himself, but must not change the position of his mouthpiece, especially if he has already attained a certain degree of proficiency, it being a known fact that there is no lack of performers who play perfectly, and who even possess a most beautiful tone, and who, nevertheless, place their mouthpiece at the side, and even at the corners of the mouth. All that can be done is to beware of acquiring this faulty habit. In short, there is no absolute rule for the position of the mouthpiece, for everything depends upon the formation of the mouth and the regularity of the teeth.[1]

The mouthpiece, once placed, must not be moved either for ascending or descending passages. It would be impossible to execute certain passages if the performer were compelled to change the position of the mouthpiece whenever he wished to take a low note after a high one in rapid succession.

The lips must never be protruded. On the contrary, the corners of the mouth must be drawn down, enabling a freer, more open tone production.[2] When the lips begin to tire the performer should never force his tones. He should then play more *piano*, because with continued loud playing the lips swell, and at last it becomes impossible to emit a note. The performer should cease to play the moment the lips begin to feel weak and fatigued; in fact, it is folly to continue playing under such circumstances, as it might lead to damage of the lip which might take a long time to cure.[3]

Attack

Always remember that the phrase *coup de langue* (stroke of the tongue) is merely a conventional expression. The tongue does not strike; on the contrary, it performs a retrograde movement, simply behaving like a valve.[4]

This should be kept in mind before placing the mouthpiece on the lips; the tongue ought to be placed against the teeth of the upper jaw in such a way that the mouth is hermetically sealed. As the tongue recedes, the column of air which was pressing against it is pushed violently into the mouthpiece causing the sound.[5]

The pronunciation of the syllable "tu" serves to determine the attack of the sound.[6] This syllable may be pronounced harder or softer, according to the degree of force to be imparted to the note. When a wedge (▼) is placed over a note:

It indicates that the sound ought to be very short; the syllable ought to be uttered very briefly and hard. When, on the contrary, there is only a dot (·):

The syllable should be pronounced more softly, so that the sounds, although detached, still form a connected phrase.

When, upon a succession of notes, there are dots over which there is a slur:

The performer should invariably strike the note with a very soft "tu," and then substitute for it the syllable "du," because the latter syllable not only distinctly articulates each note, but also serves admirably to join the notes together.

These are the only three methods of commencing or, as it is called, "attacking" the sound. Further on the various articulations will be fully explained, but for the present, it is only necessary to know and to practice single tonguing. The student's future excellence as a performer depends entirely upon this starting point.

As I already stated, the method of attacking the sound will immediately show whether the performer has a good or faulty

1 With better understanding of the physical mechanics today, many players today have changed or adjusted their embouchure in order to help improve tone, range, or endurance. While it takes patience and time to work through a change, it is more common for players to make successful adjustments now than it was during Arban's time. For students, a teacher should help you through the process. (Hooten/Marotta)

2 This is not common practice now. Most successful performers play with firm corners, and they are usually in their natural position, or slightly back, yet not as far back as in a "smile" position. The corners should move as little as possible between registers, while keeping the center of the lips flexible. (Hooten/Marotta)

3 Arban makes a great point that a player should never force their tone. Once proper form has been sacrificed, continuing to practice will reinforce bad habits. If proper form is being maintained, then slight fatigue can help to build endurance. It is important to take breaks often, in order to avoid physical and mental fatigue, which can lead to bad form and possible injury. (Hooten/Marotta)

4 This should not be imagined like a trumpet valve. The tongue movement is minimal (whether in soft or loud passages), so that it does not obstruct the air stream too much. (Hooten/Marotta)

5 What Arban is referring to is creating compression behind the tongue before releasing the air. This may be a beneficial tool at certain times; however, it shouldn't be relied upon as the default way to produce a note. (Hooten/Marotta)

6 The translation of Arban's "tu" can often be misunderstood. The French pronunciation of "tu ku" translates closer in English to "tee kee." The "ee" pronunciation requires the tongue to be in a higher and more forward position than the "u" vowel sound. However, when forming the "ee" syllable, be sure not to pull the tongue too far back in the mouth, which causes the position to be too high in the mouth. When practicing to find the optimum tongue position for each individual, practice with very small incremental change. This may help in understanding the actual syllable; however, it is even more important to understand that this syllable is more of an imitation of the sound of an energized air stream, as opposed to a vocal pronunciation of the syllable without the follow through of air. It's important to remember that when experimenting with physical changes, one must make sure to keep an ear on the result. (Hooten/Marotta)

style.[7] The first part of this method is entirely devoted to studies of this type, and the subject of slurring will be introduced only after the pupil has thoroughly mastered the striking of the note.

Breathing

Having placed the mouthpiece on the lips, open the mouth partly at the sides and pull the tongue back so as to allow the air to penetrate into the lungs. In inhaling, the stomach should not swell, but rather contract in proportion to the chest which expands.

The tongue should then advance against the teeth of the upper jaw in such a way as to hermetically seal the mouth, as though it were a valve intended to keep the column of air in the lungs.[8]

The instant the tongue recedes, the air which has been pressing against it suddenly pushes itself into the instrument and determines the vibrations which produce the sound. In exhaling, the stomach should then gradually resume its original position in proportion to the chest which relaxes.[9]

The breathing ought to be regulated by the length of the passage to be played. The longer the passage, the deeper the breath. In short phrases, if the breath is taken too deeply, or repeated too often, it produces a suffocation caused by the weight of the column of air pressing too heavily on the lungs. Therefore, the student should learn, as early as possible, to manage his breathing skillfully so as to reach the end of a long phrase without depriving a single note of its full power and firmness.[10]

Style: Faults To Be Avoided

The first matter to which the student should give special attention is the proper production of the tone. This is the basis of all good playing, and a musician whose method of producing tone is faulty will never become a great artist.

In playing softly as well as loudly, the "attack" of the sound ought to be free, clear and immediate. In striking the tone it is always necessary to articulate the syllable "tu," and not "doua," as is the habit of many players. This latter articulation causes the tone to be flat, and imparts to it a thick and disagreeable quality.

After acquiring the proper methods of tone production, the player must strive to attain a good style. By style is meant, not a lofty abstract ideal only achieved by the greatest artists, but a practical musical competence so essential for the student's mastery of his instrument. To be natural, to be correct, to play music as it is written, to phrase according to the style and sentiment of the piece performed, these are qualities which should be of the piece performed; these are qualities which should be of constant concern to the student. He cannot hope to attain them, however, until he understands and completely masters the concept of strictly observing the full value of every note as it is played. The neglect of this discipline is so common especially among military bandsmen, that it becomes necessary to discuss fully the evils which arise from it while still showing the correct performance practice.

For instance, in a measure of $\frac{2}{4}$ time consisting of four eighth notes which should be played with perfect equality by pronouncing:

Performers often make an effort to prolong the fourth eighth note by pronouncing:

If in this same rhythm a phrase begins with an ascending eighth note, too much importance will be given to the first note, which has, in fact, no more value than the others. It should be played as follows with each note being duly separated:

Instead of prolonging the first note, as shown below.

In $\frac{6}{8}$ time the same errors prevail. The sixth eighth note of each measure is prolonged; in fact, the entire six are performed in a skipping and uneven manner. The performer should play:

Instead of:

7 When Arban uses the words "faulty style," he is referring to faulty production. The lips should respond with ease, resulting in an attack that is clean, clear, and immediate. (Hooten/Marotta)

8 In regards to tongue placement when breathing, see footnote no. 13. (Hooten/Marotta)

9 It is now more common practice to simply have a natural and relaxed inhale. When breathing in the way that Arban describes, this can cause excess tension in the body, which can negatively impact both the inhale and exhale. (Hooten/Marotta)

10 In order to play a long phrase with "full power and firmness," as Arban states, one must support even more as the breath is running out. Imagine a balloon: It is filled with air and you are holding the end, which represents the aperture. In order to keep the air pressure the same at the end, you must press the air out of the balloon with your arms as it deflates. This can be applied to breathing by continuing to support with your abdominal muscles even more as you have less air to use. Breathing should be as simple as possible: a natural inhale with an energized and steady exhale that doesn't involve any tension in the chest, shoulders, or neck. It is common today for students and professionals to incorporate breathing exercises into their daily routine. Good breathing habits are a necessity to create a solid foundation in brass playing. (Hooten/Marotta)

Other players, again, play as though there were dotted eighth notes followed by sixteenths:

From these few remarks alone the reader can readily see how much the general style of a player will be influenced by faulty articulation. Remember that the tongue stands in nearly the same relation to brass instruments as the bow to stringed instruments. Accordingly, if you articulate unevenly, you are transmitting to the notes emitted into the instrument uneven and irregularly pronounced syllables which in turn result in faulty rhythms.

In accompaniments, too, an unacceptable method of playing off-beats exists. Thus in $\frac{3}{4}$ time each note should be performed with perfect evenness, without shortening or prolonging either of the two notes which make up this kind of accompaniment. For instance:

Instead of playing, as is often the case:

In $\frac{6}{8}$ time an equally faulty method of playing off-beats exists. This consists in uttering the first note of the off-beat as though it were a sixteenth note, instead of giving the same value to both notes. The performer should play:

And not:

A major shortcoming is also found in the playing of syncopated passages, especially among military bandsmen, and that is, the accenting of the second half of the syncopated note. A syncopated passage should be played by pronouncing:

And not:

There is no reason why the middle of a syncopated note should be played with greater force than the beginning. While it is essential that the starting point should be distinctly heard, the note should be sustained evenly throughout its entire value, without increasing its volume toward the middle.

The following illustration must be played in strict time without rushing the pronunciation of the syllables:

Moreover, the first eighth note should be separated from the two sixteenths as if by a sixteenth rest:

And not, as is often the case, by dragging the first note and producing faulty tonguing such as:

Later on the student will learn to perform the same passages with the correct tonguing, but at first the tongue must be trained to express lightly every variety of rhythm, without making use of this kind of articulation.

In addition to the rhythmic faults just discussed many other failings exist, almost all of which stem from the student's ill-directed ambition, bad taste, or a tendency to exaggerate. Many players imagine they are performing with intense feeling when they spasmodically increase the volume of tones or introduce tremolos by shaking their heads.

A highly sensitive and effective tremolo can be achieved by a slight movement of the right hand but this practice should not be overused lest it become a serious fault rather than an effective expression as intended.[1]

This also applies to the portamento preceded by a grace note as well as the improper playing of the turn. Some players are unable to play four consecutive notes without introducing one or two portamentos, a very unacceptable habit.

This concludes the review of the most conspicuous and striking defects resulting from a faulty style. It is hoped that the students will avoid these shortcomings and carefully practice the remedies discussed above. Always remember: Constant attention to good practices and continual correction is required in the beginning stages of study to establish the very finest performance habits.

1 Arban's use of the word tremolo is referring to vibrato. It is no longer common practice to use the hand in order to create vibrato. Pulsing the air is also not effective or efficient. The most common method is by a very slight movement of the aperture or jaw. Varying speeds of vibrato can be used to enhance or color a musical passage. (Hooten/Marotta)

I. First Studies

Explanatory Notes on the First Studies

In Study No. 1 start or "attack" the sound by pronouncing the syllable "tu;" keep it well sustained and at the same time give it all the strength and brilliancy possible. (See footnote no. 13.)

Under no circumstances should the cheeks ever be puffed out nor should the lips make noise in the mouthpiece even though many performers appear to think otherwise. The sound forms itself; it should be "struck" firmly using proper lip tension so as to be accurately in tune.

Studies nos. 7 and 8 deal with all of the notes produced by using the same valves. Studies nos. 9 and 10 take the student through all of the keys and so the required fingerings have been thoroughly indicated. These lessons should be practiced over a long period so that the student may become completely secure with the fingering of the instrument. From this point on it will not be necessary to mark the numbers of the valves under each note although fingerings will appear in passages throughout the book where it will facilitate a performance.

Throughout Studies nos. 1–50, be sure to strike each sound and give each note its full value.

Syncopation

Syncopation occurs when the accent falls upon the light instead of the heavy beat of a measure. Always remember that the accented note must be sustained throughout its full value and, while the beginning of the note should be duly marked, the second half of the duration of a note should never be cut short.

Many students have great difficulty mastering syncopation. Study carefully the solution of the rhythm problem appearing over each study. A passage of this kind should be played as follows:

And not:

Rhythmic Figure

In these studies the eighth note should be held for its full value. Be sure never to substitute a rest for the dot. The player should play:

And not as though it were written:

Rhythmic Figure

In order to lend lightness to these studies, the first eighth note should be played in a shorter manner than its indicated value. It should be executed like a sixteenth note with a rest being introduced between it and the two sixteenths which follow it. The passage is written:

And should be played thus:

The same applies to an eighth note following, instead of preceding, the sixteenth.

Written:

Should be played thus:

Written:

Should be played thus:

$\frac{6}{8}$ Meter

In $\frac{6}{8}$ time, the eighth notes should be well separated, and should have equal value allotted to each of them. Consequently, the third eighth note in each measure should never be dragged out as some players are inclined to do.

Dotted eighths, and eighths followed by sixteenths are played in this rhythm, by observing the same rules discussed above in $\frac{2}{4}$ time.

---

2 The suggested length and articulation marks are valid styles that are still used today, although these suggestions should not be thought of as the player's default. One should always practice a variety of styles and articulations so that they will remain musically flexible. (Hooten/Marotta)

First Studies

*Apply the same tempo to studies nos. 1 to 10.

9.

10.
0
2
1
1
2
1
3
2
♩ = c. 60–108 (11–15)
11.
simile

12.
13.
14.
simile
15.
simile
♩ = c. 76–132 (16–19)
16.
simile

17.
simile
18.
simile
19.
♩ = c. 92–140 (20–27)
20.
21.

22.
23.
24.
25.

26.
27.
♩ = c. 68–120 (28–40)
28.
29.
simile

30.
simile
31.
simile
32.
simile
33.
simile

34.
simile
35.
simile
36.
simile

37.
simile
38.
simile

39.
simile
40.
simile
♩ = c. 64–100 (41–45)
41.

42.
43.
44.
45.
𝅗𝅥 = c. 60–92
46.
sempre staccato

2
0
♩ = c. 72–112 (47–49)
47.
simile

48.
simile
49.
simile
♩ = c. 60–116
50.
simile
Fine
Da Capo

Syncopation*

* Refer to page 5.

♩ = c. 96 – 124
7.
♩ = c. 100 – 132
8.
♩ = c. 116
9.
simile
Allegro ♩ = c. 96 – 120
10.
simile

♩ = c. 124
11.
simile
♩ = c. 128
12.
simile

Rhythmic Figure ♩. ♪*

* Refer to page 5.

♩ = c. 96–140
16.
Tempo di Mazurka ♩ = c. 72–116
17.

* Refer to page 5.

♩ = c. 72–120
20.
tu tu tu tu tu tu tu
mp
simile
EVEN AIR STREAM, UNDER ARTICULATION
♩ = c. 76–124
21.
mp
simile
♩ = c. 68–120
22.
mp
simile

♩ = c. 68–116
23.
mp
tu tu tu tu tu tu tu tu tu tu tu
♩ = c. 76–124
24.
tu tu tu tu tu tu tu tu tu tu
mp
simile
♩ = c. 68–120
25.
tu tu tu tu tu tu
mp
simile

♩ = c. 72–124
26.
mf
simile
♩ = c. 68–120
27.
mf
simile

$\frac{6}{8}$ Meter*

* Refer to pages 2 and 5.

Allegretto ♩. = c. 64–108
30.
p
f
p
rall.
a tempo
f
p
f
Allegretto ♩. = c. 52–96
31.
mf
simile

Allegretto ♩. = c. 60–116
32.
tu tu tu tu tu tu tu
mp
simile
Allegretto ♩. = c. 52–96
33.
tu tu tu tu tu tu tu tu
mp
simile

♩. = c. 60–100
34.
mp
simile
♩. = c. 68–108
35.
mp
simile

Allegretto ♩. = c. 56–96
36.
tu tu tu tu tu tu tu tu tu tu tu
mf
simile
♩. = c. 58–100
37.
mp
simile

♪ = c. 104 – ♩. = 60
38.
p (mf)

II. Slurring or Legato Playing

Undoubtedly, slurring is one of the most important aspects of this method. Considerable space has been allotted to it, particularly to explaining those studies realized exclusively by lip movement without the addition or substitution of valves. The fingering must be followed exactly, no matter how unusual it may seem. Although not recommended for use in actual performance, this fingering was purposely designed to increase the difficulty of the study and to oblige the lips to move in producing the different pitches without using the valves. This study, moreover, is analogous to that practiced by singers when they study the movement of the glottis in order to master the trill.

The easiest interval to slur is the minor second. Slurring the major second is more difficult, since some lip movement is needed. Slurring the third is most difficult, since it often involves pitches where valves cannot possibly be used to help slur from the lower to the higher note. By diligent practice, this study will become the basis for fluent and brilliant playing. It imparts great suppleness to the lips and is an essential aid for mastering the trill.

Trilling by means of the lips is only desirable for intervals whose harmonics lie a second apart, as in Study no. 23, and then only if the indicated fingering is followed; otherwise trills in thirds will result and these are both annoying and objectionable.[20]

The main purpose of Studies nos. 1–15 of this section is to teach slurring. In order to achieve this properly, swell the lower note slightly and at the moment it reaches its dynamic peak slur it up to the higher note by a slight pressure of the mouthpiece on the lips.

Next follows the practicing of thirds which is obtained by the tension of the muscles and also by pressure of the mouthpiece on the lips.[21] The notes should be produced with perfect equality; they must be connected with each other with absolute evenness and played precisely in time and with the exact fingering shown.

Studies nos. 16–69 are for the purpose of learning how to slur thirds with ease so as to enable the student to play grace notes and double appoggiaturas with elegance later on. Since both these ornaments are produced only through lip movement, a few examples have been included herein, although they will be treated in greater detail under the section on Grace Notes in Section IV.

20 Although it may be called a lip trill, the trill is controlled by a consistent air flow and movement of the tongue. (Hooten/Marotta)

21 The "slight pressure of the mouthpiece on the lips" should be replaced by a change in tongue position. Arban eludes to this when he writes the syllables "Taw Eee" seen on the following page in Study no. 3. (Hooten/Marotta)

Studies on Slurring or Legato Playing

* All of the exercises in this section should be practiced using the syllables "Taw Eee" with a little more air on the top note. The trilling exercises from no. 22 on are accompanied in the same way.

♩ = c. 116
7.
simile
simile
♩ = c. 116
8.
simile
simile
♩ = c. 116
9.
simile
simile
♩ = c. 116
10.
simile
simile
♩ = c. 116
11.
simile
♩ = c. 116
12.

13.
♩ = c. 96
14.
Allegretto ♩ = c. 104
mp
rall.
a tempo
15.
Andante ♩ = c. 72
p

♩ = c. 116
16.
♩ = c. 116
17.
♩ = c. 112–124
18.
♩ = c. 112 – 124
19.

20.
♩ = c. 112–124
21.
♩ = c. 112 – 124
6

♩ = c. 96–116

22.

2
3
2
3
0
0
1
2
1
2
1
1
2
2
0
0

♩ = c. 116
23.
Allegro ♩ = c. 140 – 𝅗𝅥 = 92
24.

Allegro ♩ = c. 128
25.
Allegro ♩ = c. 124
26.

♩ = c. 108
27.
3 0 3 0 3 0 3 0 3 0 3
0
1
2

♩ = c. 96
28.

♩ = c. 96
29.
♩ = c. 84 – 100
30.

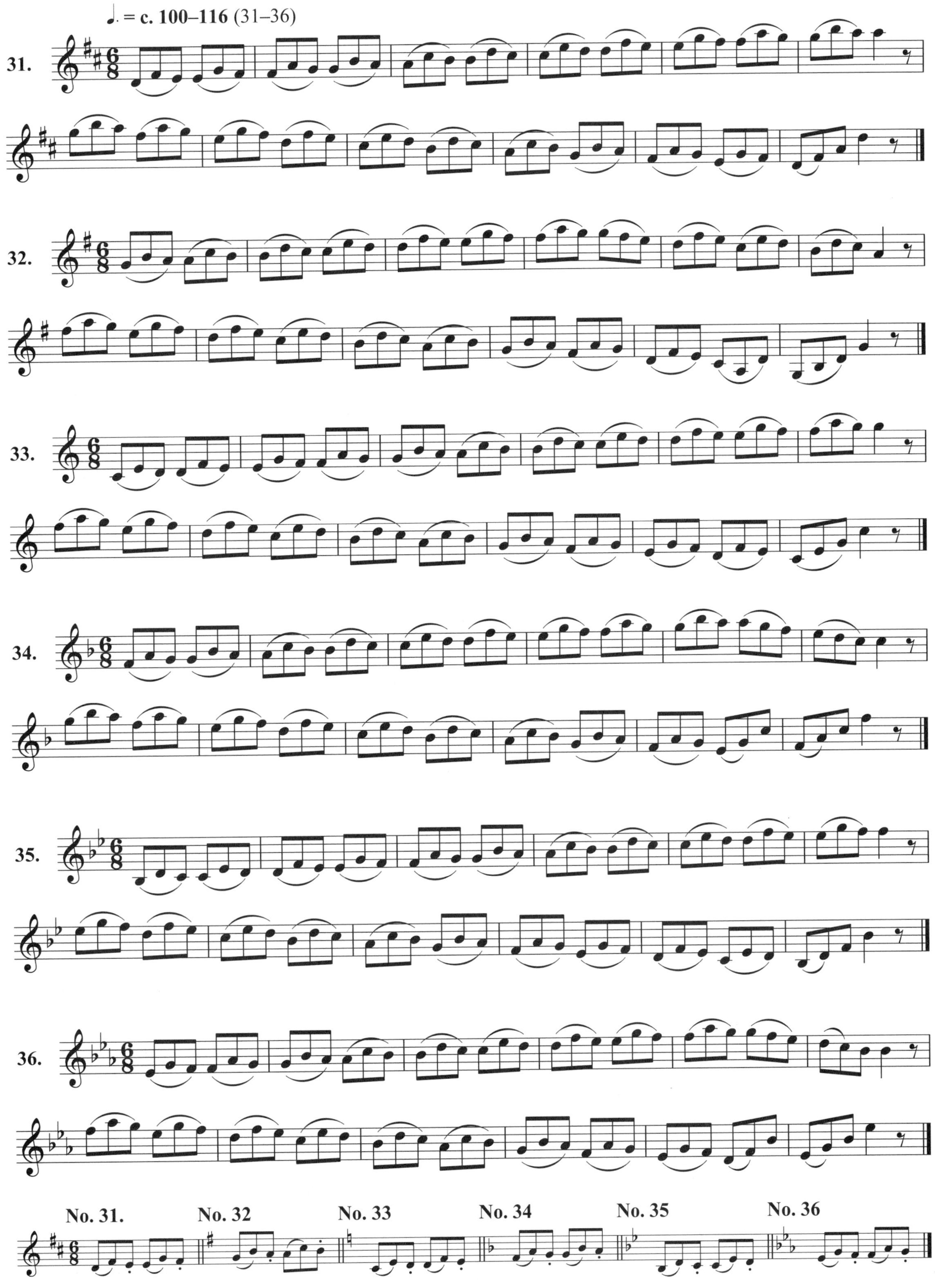
♩. = c. 100–116 (31–36)
31.
32.
33.
34.
35.
36.
No. 31.
No. 32
No. 33
No. 34
No. 35
No. 36

♩ = c. 116 (37–42)
37.
38.
39.
40.
41.
42.
No. 37
No. 38
No. 39
No. 40
No. 41
No. 42
No. 37
No. 38
No. 39
No. 40
No. 41
No. 42

♩. = c. 88–116 (43–48)
43.
44.
45.
46.
47.
48.
No. 43
No. 44
No. 45
No. 46
No. 47
No. 48

♩ = c. 80–100 (49–54)
49.
50.
51.
52.
53.
54.
No. 49
No. 50
No. 51
No. 52
No. 53
No. 54
No. 49
No. 50
No. 51
No. 52
No. 53
No. 54

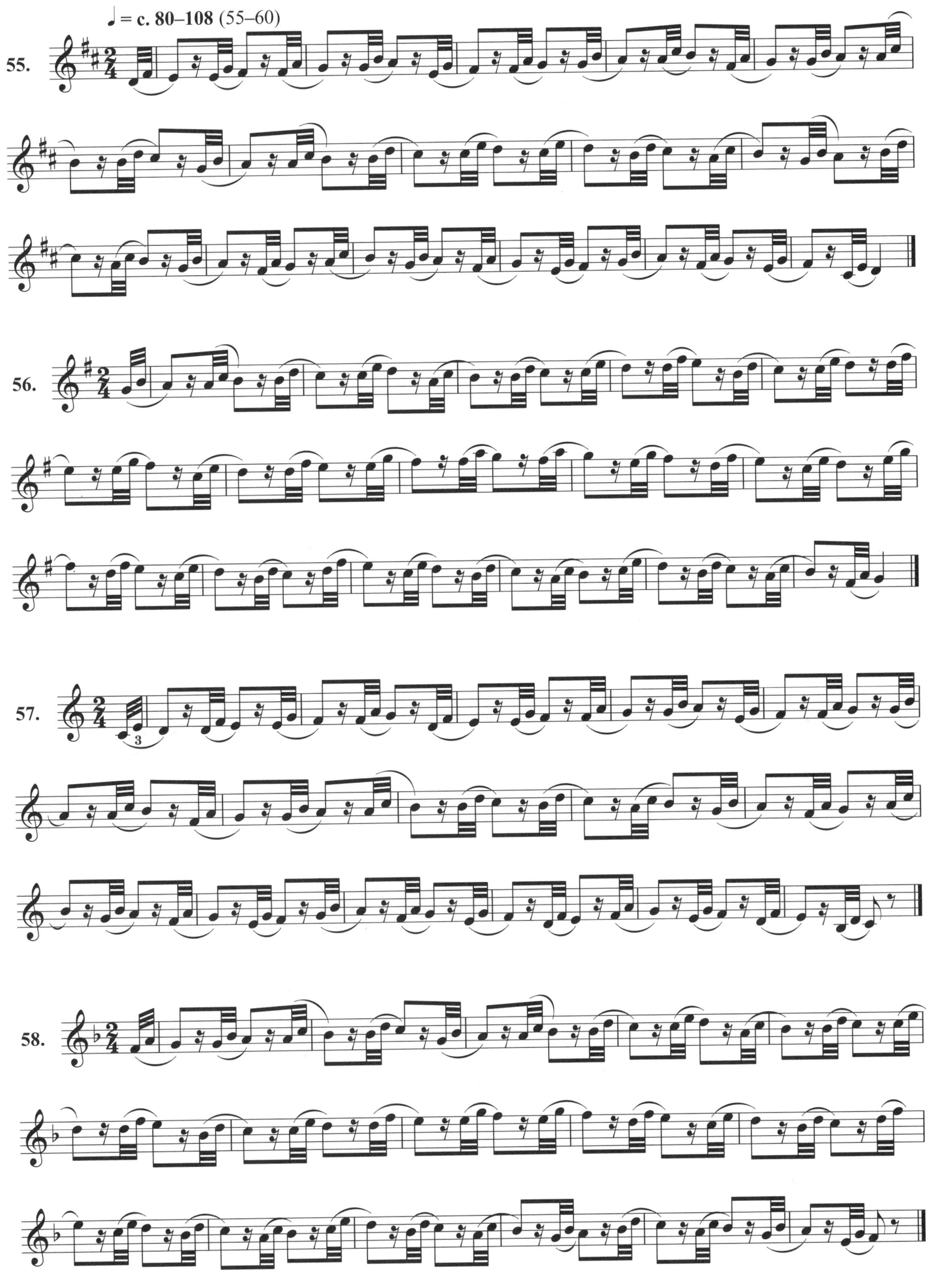
♩ = c. 80–108 (55–60)
55.
56.
57.
3
58.

8va ad libitum
59.
60.
Allegro ♩. = c. 104–124 (61–63)
61.
3
62.

Allegro
63.
Fine
D.C.
♩. = c. 88–100
64.

♩ = c. 112
65.
♩ = c. 112
66.
Allegretto grazioso ♩ = c. 116
67.

♩ = c. 112
68.

♩ = c. 112–128
69.

III. Scales

Major Scales

The study of scales, as a rule, has been greatly neglected in other methods. Usually a few examples are provided, leaving the student to learn by himself whatever is missing from the method. As a result, only a few players are able to play scales properly. However, the diligent practice of scales should not be neglected. Its importance has justified treating the scales thoroughly in all twelve major keys. By this means, a perfectly even tone as well as a legato and correct method of playing can be achieved.

Minor Scales

Due to their secondary nature, minor scales are given a more limited treatment. Through studies based on the tonic and dominant, the student will become familiar with them.[22]

Chromatic Scales and Triplets

Due to its importance, the chromatic scale has been treated at considerable length below. Through its study, nimble fingering can be achieved. Make sure to press the valves down firmly in order to produce all the notes fully.

Practice slowly at first, stressing the rhythmic pattern indicated. It is necessary to grow louder in the ascending and softer in the descending portion of the scale. Play in strict time and do not rush the last part of the phrase as some players do. Use of the metronome is recommended in order to achieve the precision necessary for a beautiful performance.

---

22 Composers today often use all forms of scales and arpeggios. It is important that students become proficient on all forms of minor scales, as well as every other type of scale. (Hooten/Marotta) Refer to *Technical Studies* (O2280) by Herbert L. Clarke; Daily *Trumpet Routines* (O4945) by Claude Gordon.

Major Scales*

* In nos. 1-78 the rhythm ♫ may be substituted with ♪. ♬ or ♬ ♪. for further study.

5.
simile
simile
6.
simile
7.
simile
8.
simile
9.
simile

10.
simile
11.
simile
simile
12.
simile
13.
simile

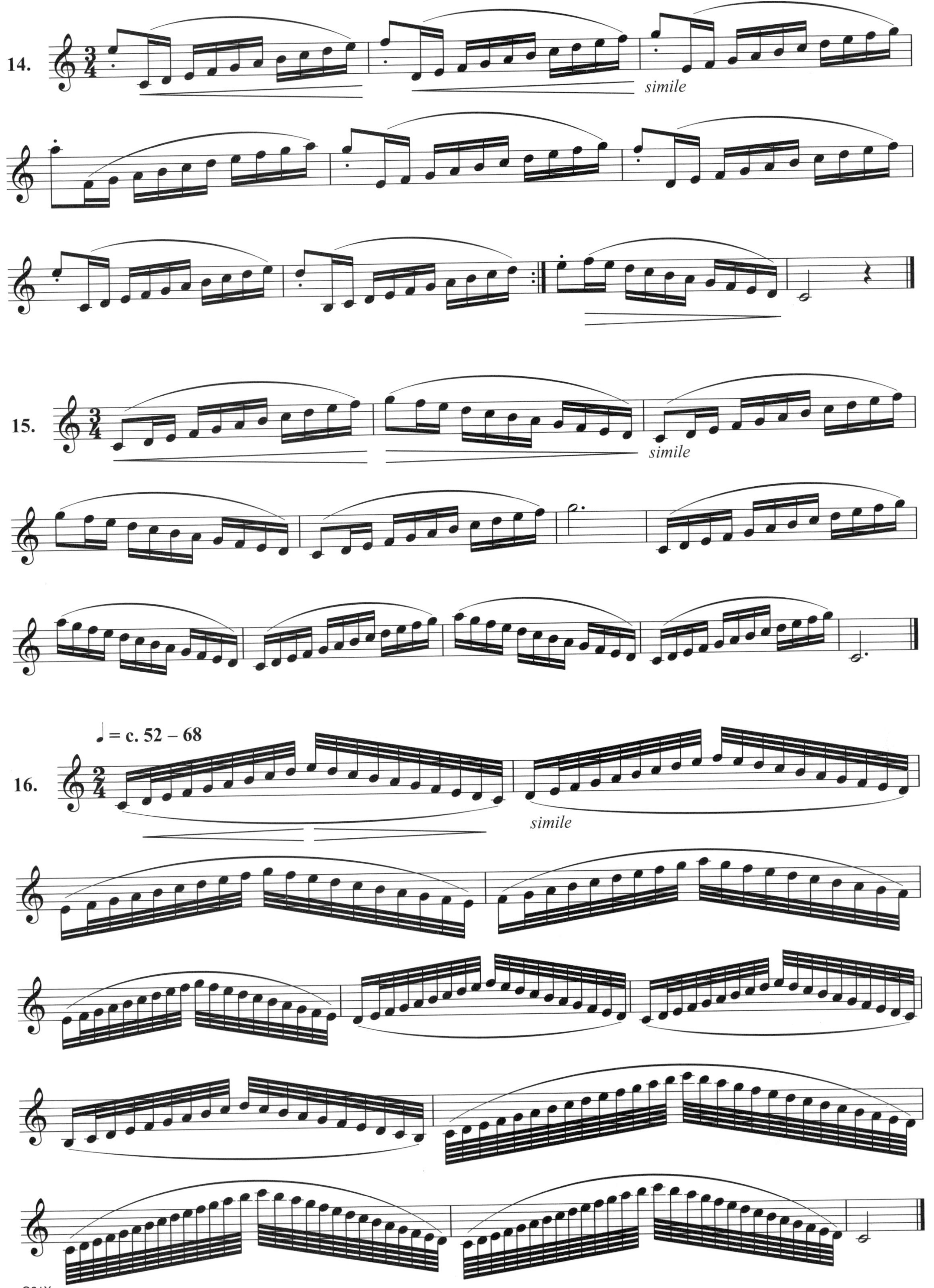
14.
simile
15.
simile
♩ = c. 52 – 68
16.
simile

F Major (transpose nos. 17–22 to F♯ major)

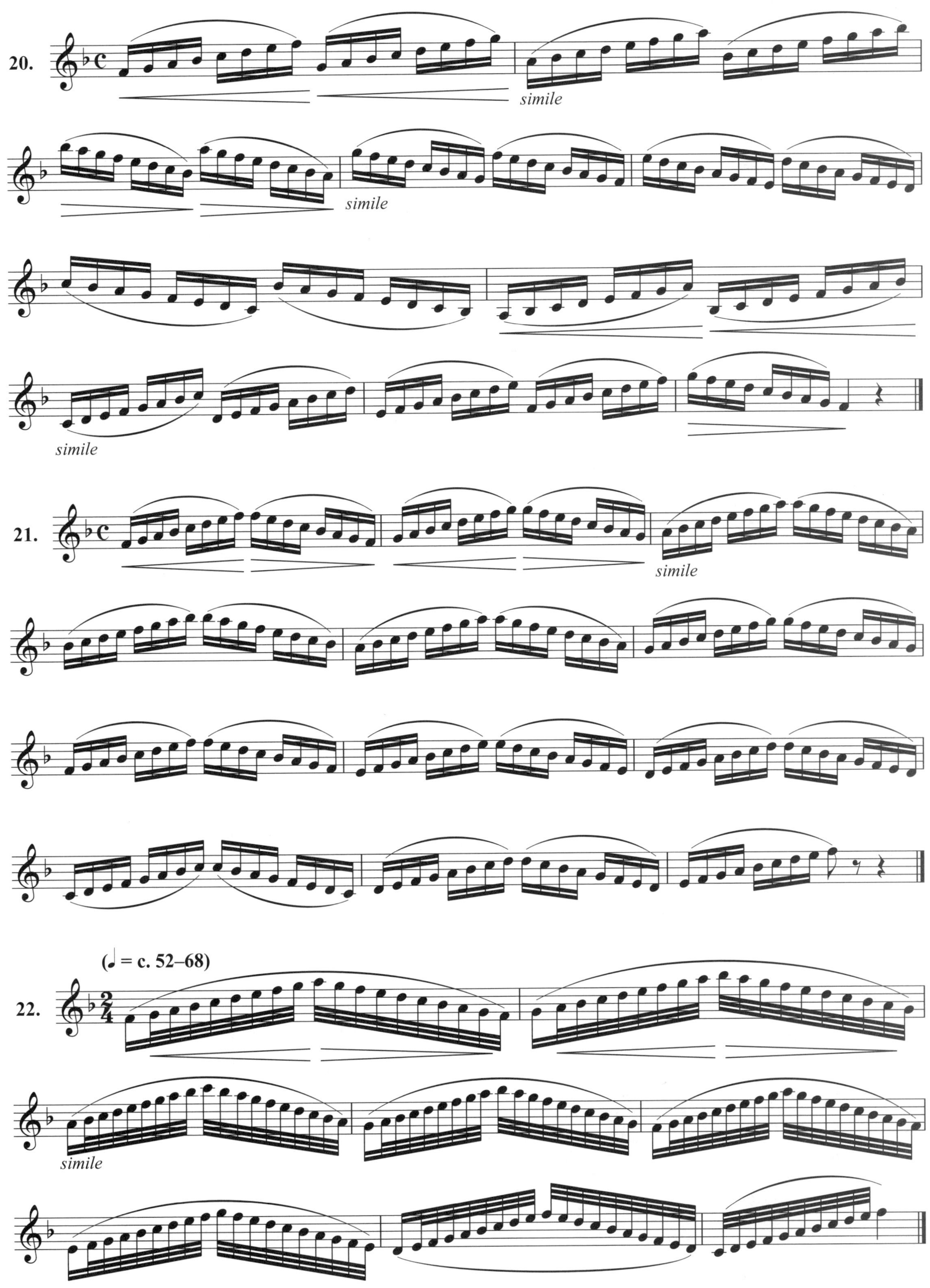
20.
simile
simile
simile
21.
simile
(𝅗𝅥 = c. 52–68)
22.
simile

B♭ Major (transpose nos. 23–28 to B major)
(♩ = c. 64–124)
23.
simile
simile
24.
simile
simile
25.
simile
26.
simile
simile

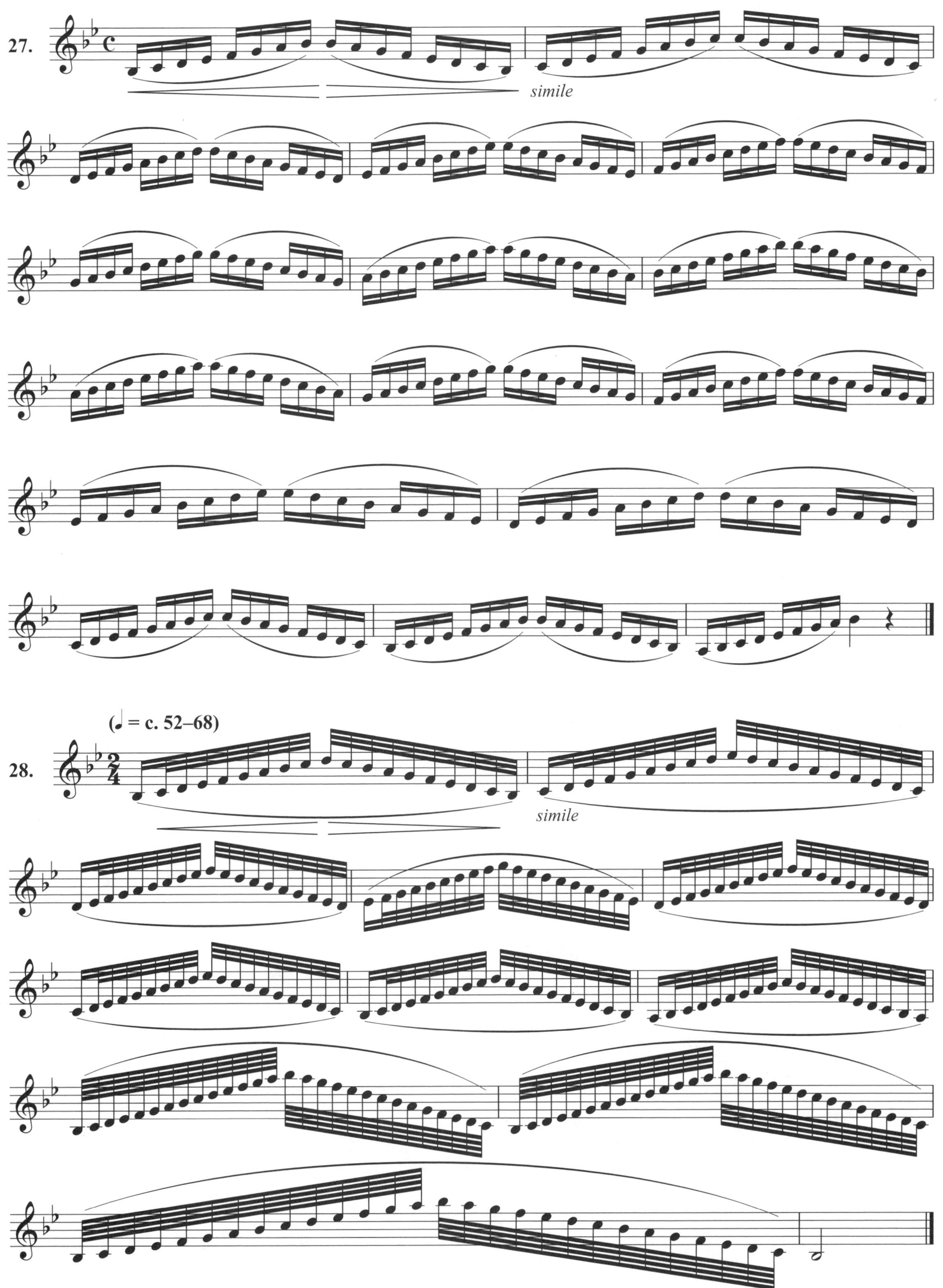
27.
simile
(♩ = c. 52–68)
28.
simile

E♭ Major
(♩ = c. 64–124)
29.
simile
simile
30.
simile
simile
31.
simile
32.
simile

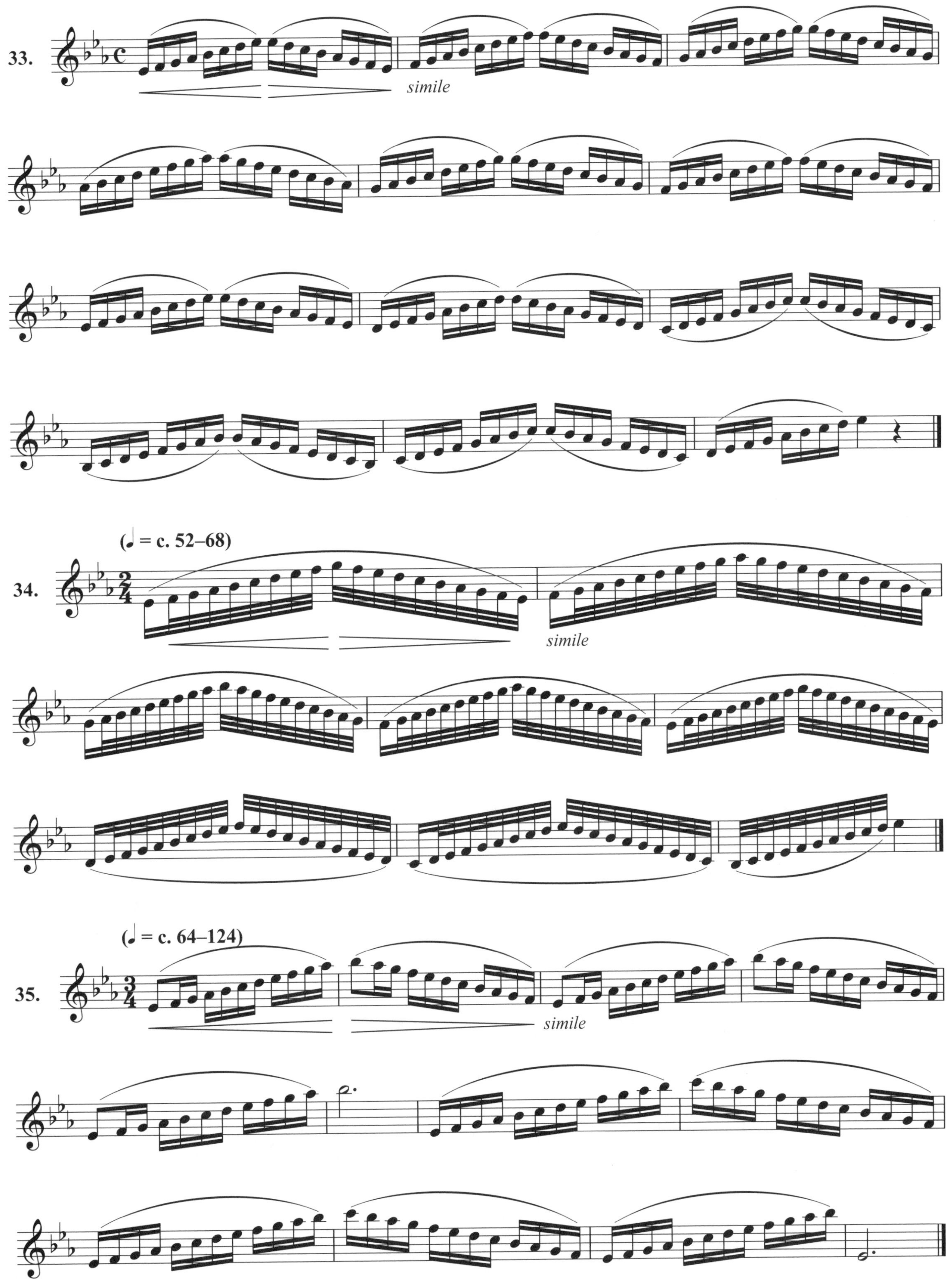
33.
simile
(♩ = c. 52–68)
34.
simile
(♩ = c. 64–124)
35.
simile

A♭ Major
36.
simile
simile
37.
simile
simile
38.
simile

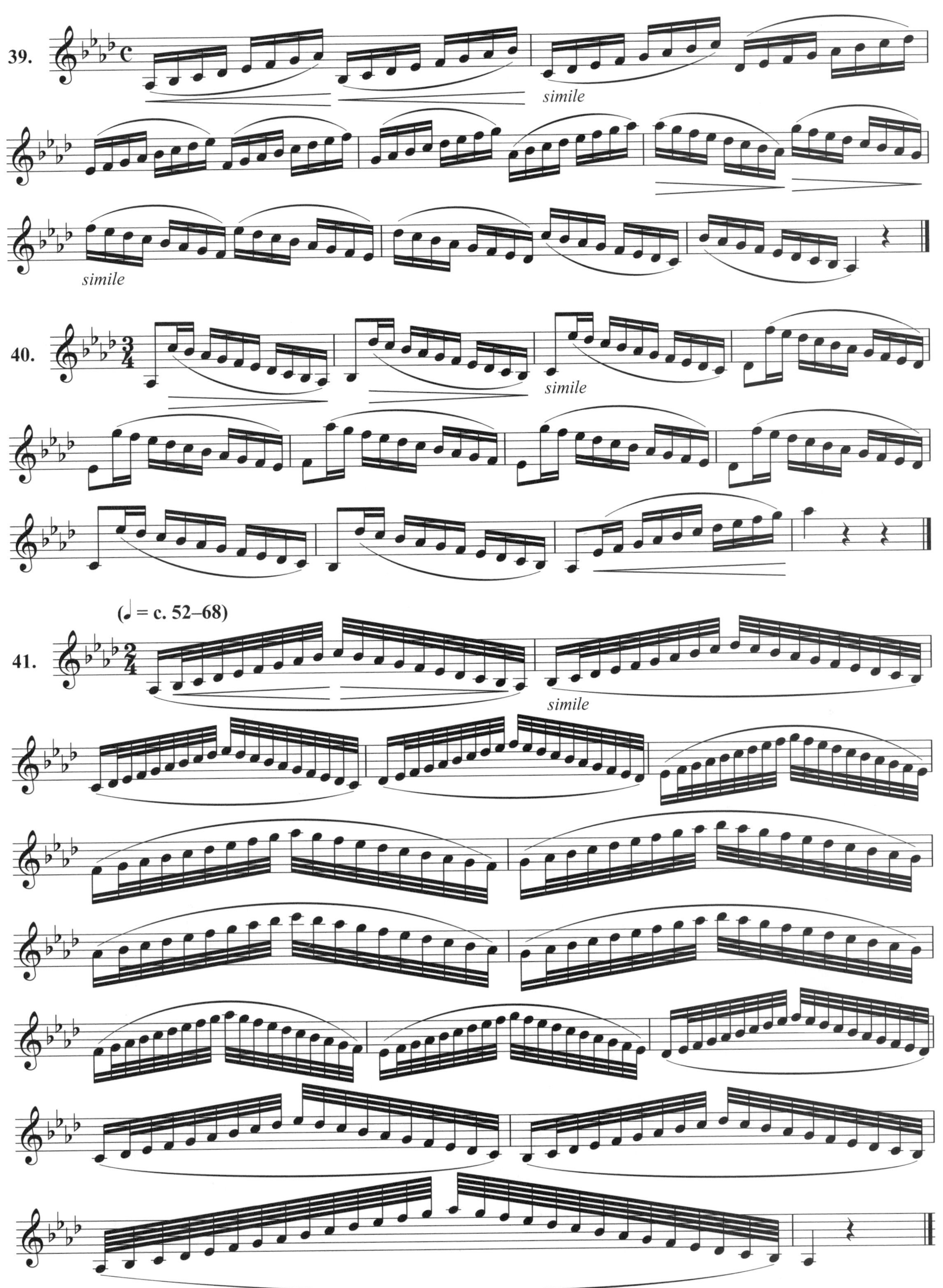
39.
simile
simile
40.
simile
(𝅗𝅥 = c. 52–68)
41.
simile

D♭ Major
(𝅗𝅥 = c. 64–124)
42.
C♯ Major
simile
simile
simile
simile
G♭ Major
43.
F♯ Major
simile
simile
simile
simile

C♭ Major
44.
B Major
simile
simile
simile
simile
E Major
45.
simile
simile
46.
simile

47.
simile
48.
simile
simile
49.
simile

(♩ = c. 52–68)
50.
simile
A Major(♩ = c. 64–124)
51.
simile
simile
52.
simile
simile
53.
simile

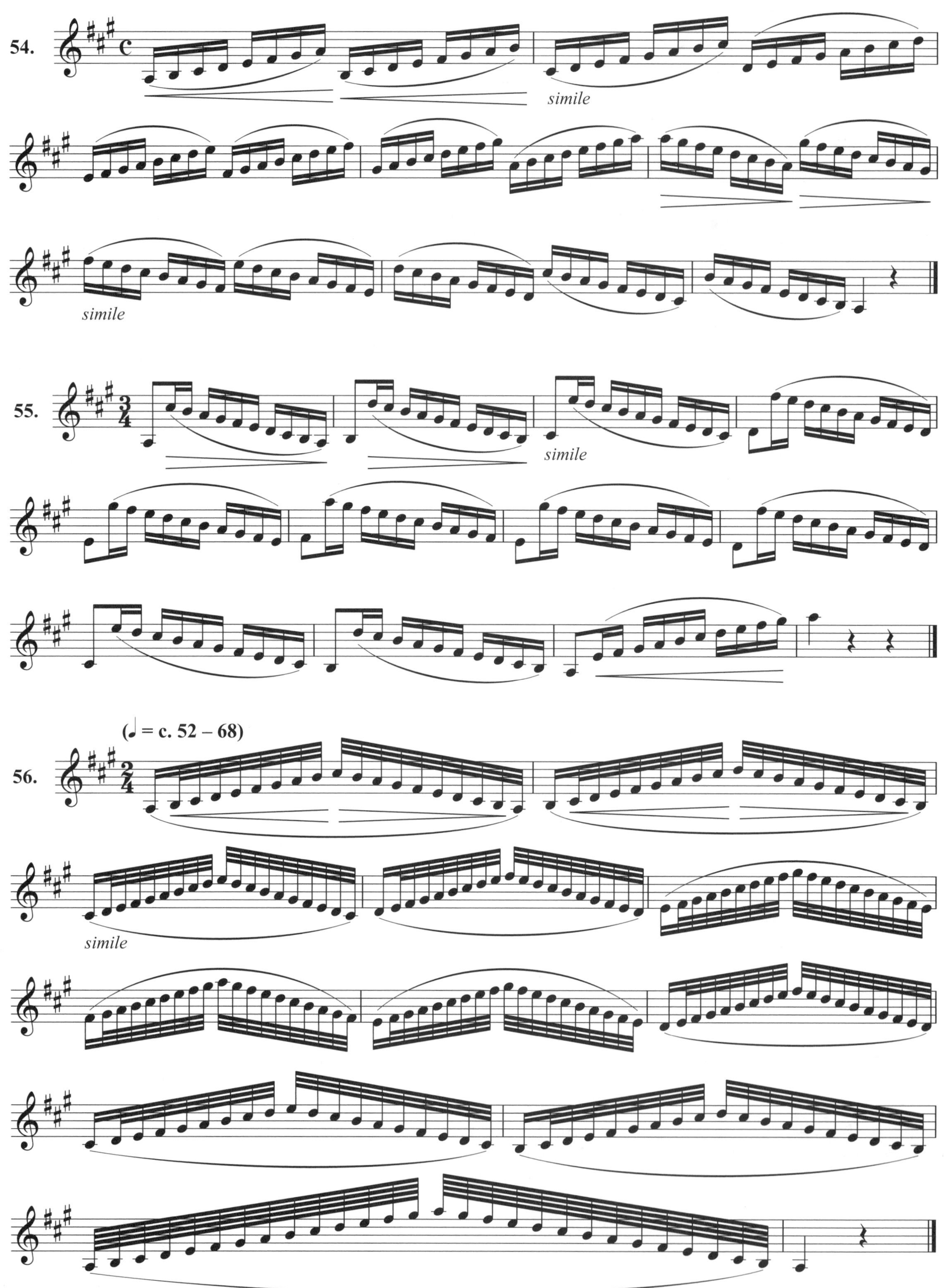
54.
simile
simile
55.
simile
(♩ = c. 52 – 68)
56.
simile

D Major
(♩ = c. 64–124)
57.
simile
simile
58.
simile
simile
59.
simile

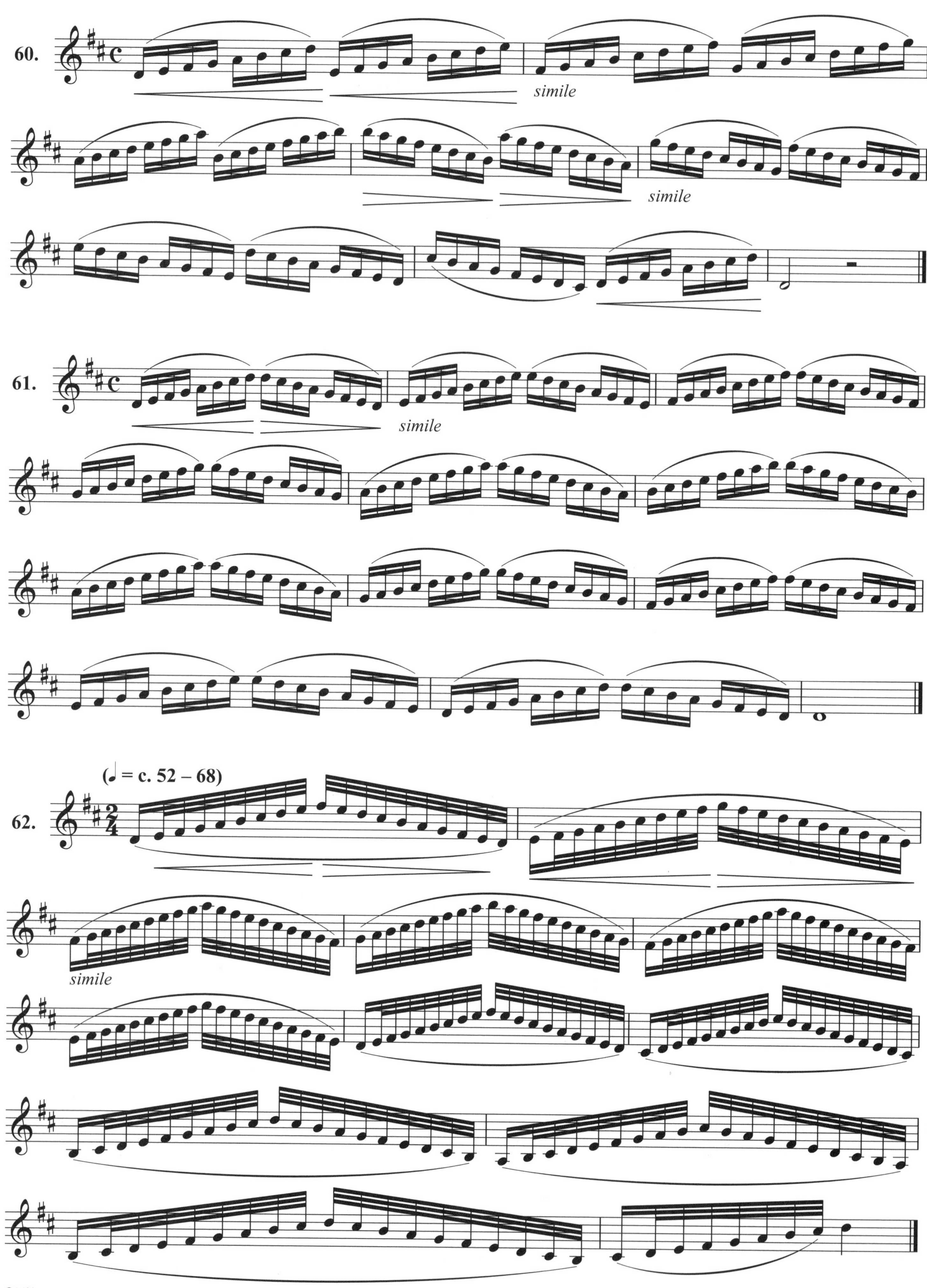

60.
simile
simile
61.
simile
(♩ = c. 52 – 68)
62.
simile

G Major
(♩ = c. 64–124)
63.
simile
simile
64.
simile
simile
65.
simile

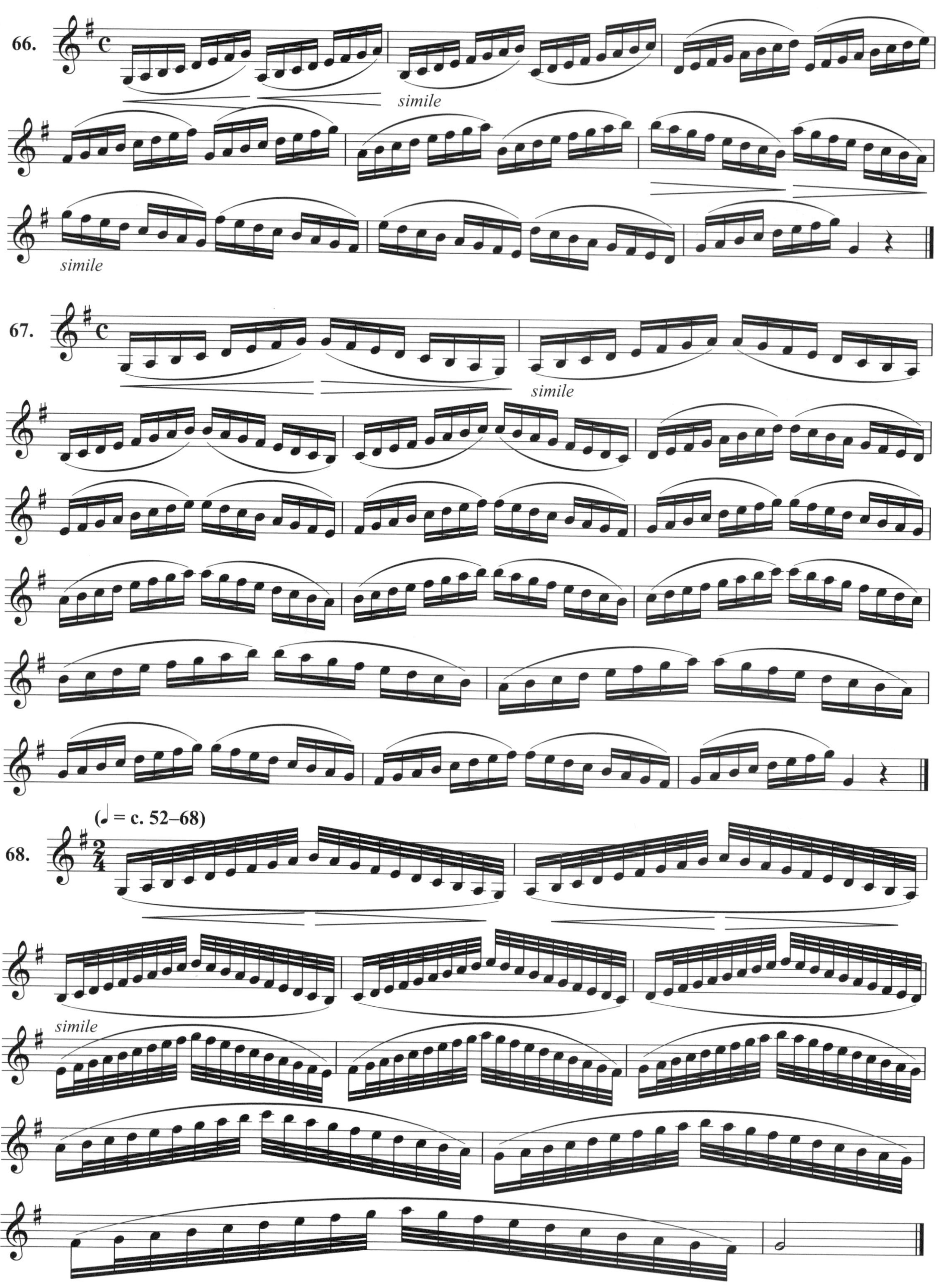
66.
simile
simile
67.
simile
(♩ = c. 52–68)
68.
simile

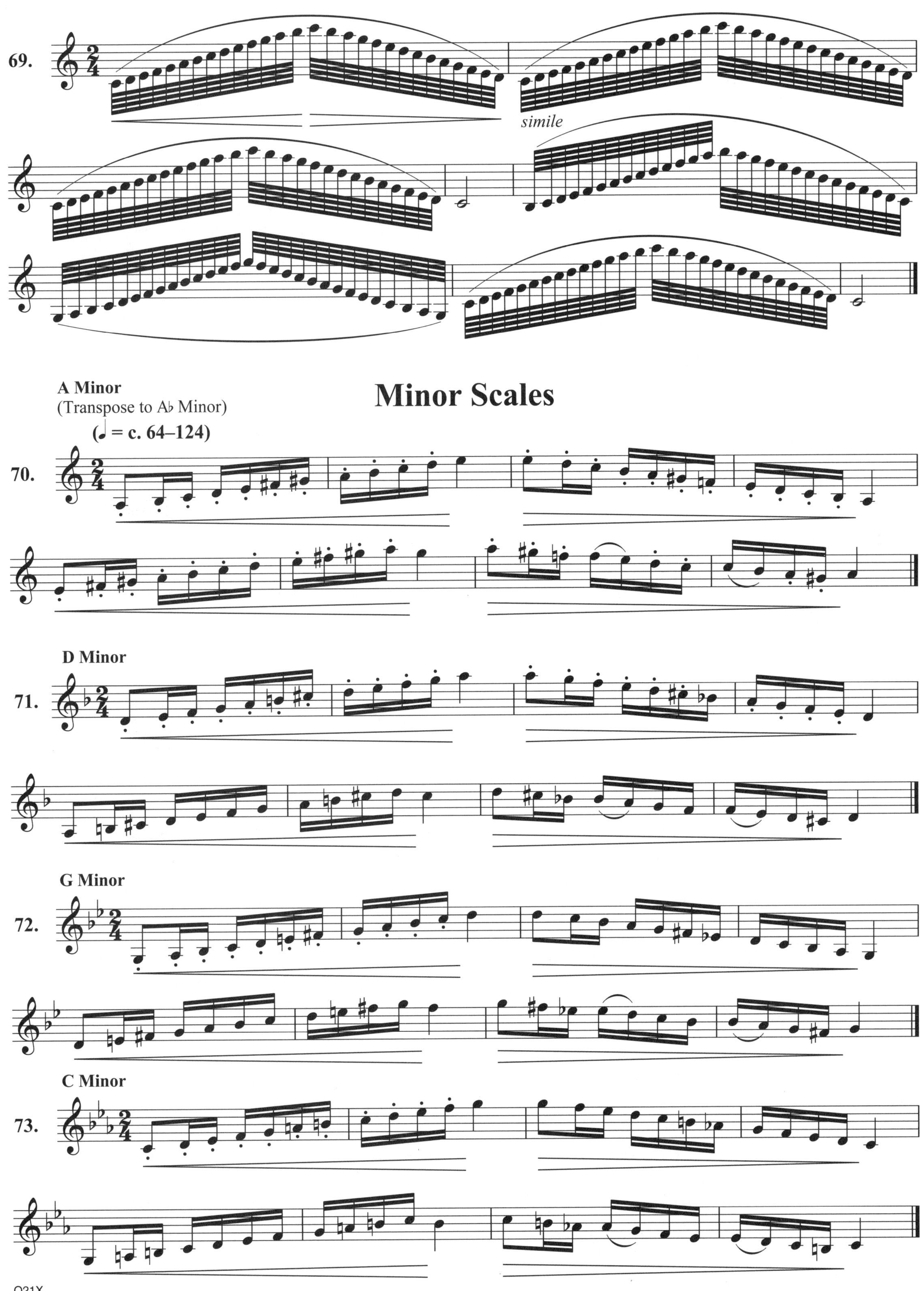
69.
simile
A Minor
(Transpose to A♭ Minor)
Minor Scales
(♩ = c. 64–124)
70.
D Minor
71.
G Minor
72.
C Minor
73.

F Minor
74.
C♯ Minor
75.
F♯ Minor
76.
B Minor
(Transpose to B♭ Minor)
77.
E Minor
(Transpose to E♭ Minor)
78.

Chromatic Scales
(♩ = c. 80–140)
1.
2.
(♩ = c. 72–140)
3.
simile

4.
3
3
3
3
simile
(𝅗𝅥 = c. 64 – 132)
5.
simile
simile

(♩ = c. 72–144)
6.
simile

7.
simile
(♩ = c. 92–140)
8.
simile

(𝅗𝅥 = c. 76–136)
9.
simile

*Apply also to studies nos. 11 to 24.

13.
14.
8va ad lib.
15.
8va ad lib.
16.

17.
8va ad lib.
18.
♩ = c. 56–100 (19–24)
19.
20.

21.
22.
23.
24.

♩ = c. 76–128
25.
simile
simile
(♩. = c. 68–120)
26.
simile
(♩ = c. 96–128)
27.

(♩. = c. 68–120) (28–30)
28.

29.

♩ = c. 56–100
31.
3
3

IV. Ornaments

The purpose of the 88 studies in this section is to prepare the student for performing grace notes and other ornaments. These studies should be practiced slowly in order to accustom the lips and fingers to play in perfect coordination with each other.

All the lessons have been specifically designed to serve as studies for all the different types of grace notes: the long and short appoggiatura; the portamento; the double appoggiatura; the turn; the trill; and the mordent. It is advisable, however, to avoid abusing them in practice, since an excess of ornaments is always in bad taste.

The Simple or Long Appoggiatura

The long appoggiatura is a grace note which does not form part of the harmony and which receives half the value of the following note (the main note), if that value is divisible by two.

Example:

Played:

The long appoggiatura may be placed above or below any note. If placed above, the long appoggiatura forms either a whole step or a half step with the main note. If below, it always forms a half step with the main note.

For instance:

In music of the old masters, from the seventeenth century to the early nineteenth century, the long appoggiatura was indicated by a small grace note which took its value from the note immediately following it. However, since the 1830s, in order to standardize its performance, the long appoggiatura is written out as a normal-sized note with the exact value that should be played. This notation is much more consistent and easier to follow (see Studies Nos. 44–47).

The Short Appoggiatura or Grace Note

The short appoggiatura is a grace note which derives its value from the following or main note. It is usually found in fast tempo. Also, its attack should be accented so that the short appoggiatura has slightly greater force than the main note. If placed above the main note, the short appoggiatura is either a whole step or a half step away from the main note.[23] If below, it is always a half step away from the main note (see Studies nos. 48–54).

Portamento

The portamento is a grace note which is, in fact, merely the repetition of a note which the player desires to connect to another by slurring. This type of ornament must not be abused. When judiciously employed, it is highly effective. But usually it is much better to slur from one note to another without using this type of grace note (see Studies nos. 55–59).

The Double Appoggiatura

There are two types of double appoggiatura. The first type consists of two grace notes which approach the main note from the same direction, beginning a third above or below the main note.

Example, ascending:

Example, descending:

The first type of double appoggiatura should take its value from the note which follows it, and not from the preceding note (see Studies nos. 36–38).

Example, ascending:

Example, descending:

The second type of double appoggiatura consists of an upper and a lower grace note which approach the main note from opposite directions.

Written:

Played:

The second type of double appoggiatura should take its value from the preceding note and note from the note which follows it (see Studies nos. 39–43).

23 Until Arban's time, the short appoggiatura was placed on the beat. Since then, it has become just as common for the grace note to be before the beat, at the composer/conductor's/performer's discretion. In regards to the grace note being accented, it is not always approached this way today. Often, the note that the grace leads to is stronger than the grace. Other times, there is no emphasis on either note. (Hooten/Marotta)

The Turn

Studies nos. 1–23 are designed to prepare the student for playing the turn. The turn consists of a group of grace notes revolving around a main note. It is necessary to give as much value to the upper and lower grace notes of the turn as to the note which serves as the pivot.

The Four-Note Turn

There are two types of four-note turn. The first is written as follows:

And played as follows:

Here in its normal position, the loop begins its curl from above, which indicates that the upper grace note is played first.

The lower grace not should always form a half step with the main note, indicated by placing an accidental beneath the sign. The upper grace note may form either a whole step or a half step with the main note, depending on the tonality of the music.

The second type of four-note turn is written as follows:

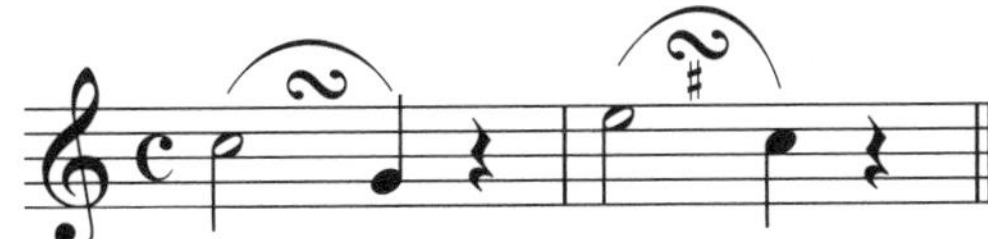

And played as follows:

Here in its inverted position, the loop begins its curl from below, which indicates that the lower grace note is played first.

This, at any rate, is the proper way to write such passages. Unfortunately, these details are presently neglected by composers and are left to the player's discretion (see Studies nos. 24–31).

The Three-Note Turn

There are two types of three-note turns: ascending and descending. In either case, they may consist of a minor or a diminished third, but never a major third. They are written as follows:

And played as follows:

The value of the three-note turn is not usually taken from the main note which follows it, but more often from the preceding beat. The turn should be played very lightly, care being taken to attack the first grace not clearly (see Studies nos. 32–35).

The Trill

On valve instruments, the trill is the most difficult of all ornaments to produce. The only really tolerable trill on the cornet or trumpet is that of a half step. However, the whole-step trill is also satisfactory. For the latter trill, be sure to press the valves down firmly so that each trill beat may be perfectly distinct. First, practice the preparatory Studies nos. 60–67 slowly and deliberately, as a means for producing a pure tone. Later on, practice the trill Studies nos. 68–80, making sure to follow the exact fingering indicated.

The Mordent

The mordent is nothing more than a shorter, quicker form of the trill. It requires neither preparation nor resolution. It is indicated by the following sign:

and played as follows:

The mordent consisting of several trill beats is almost impracticable on the cornet. The player must, therefore, restrict himself to the mordent with one trill beat which is much easier to play and very graceful.

Played:

The mordent takes it rhythmic value from the note to which it belongs (see Studies nos. 81–88).

Preparatory Studies for the Turn

♩ = c. 80–120
2.

♩ = c. 80–120
3.

♩ = c. 80–120 (4–7)
4.
1
2
1
2
5.
3
3
1
2
3
1
2
6.
1
2
2
3
1
2
1
2

7.
8.
♩ = c. 120 – 𝅗𝅥 = c. 116

♩ = c. 72–120 (9–16)
9.
10.
11.

12.
1
2
1
2
0
13.
3
14.

15.
16.
♩ = c. 112 – 𝅗𝅥. = c. 80 (17–22)
17.

18.
3
3
1
2
1
2
3
19.
20.
3
1
2

21.
22.
23.
♪ = c. 132 – ♩. = c. 96

The Turn

Andante ♩ = c. 64
26.
Allegro moderato ♩ = c. 92
27.

Fine
D.C.
Andante ♩ = c. 64
28.
1
2
3

Allegretto ♩ = c. 88
29.
3
3
3
3
3
3

Andantino ♩ = c. 72
30.
Fine
1
2
3
1
2
3
D.C.
Allegretto ♩ = c. 80
31.
simile

Andantino ♩ = c. 72
32.
Fine
Più mosso ♩ = c. 92
D.C.
Allegretto ♩ = c. 96
33.
Fine
D.C.
Andante ♪ = c. 108
34.

Allegro moderato ♩ = c. 92–112
35.
The Double Appoggiatura
Andante ♪ = c. 108
36.
rall.
Tempo I
rall.
Andantino ♩ = c. 80
37.
rall.

Allegretto ♩ = c. 96
38.
rall.
Fine
rall.
D.C.
Allegretto moderato ♩. = c. 72
39.
Andante con spirito ♩ = c. 84
40.
rall.

Allegretto ♩. = c. 92
41.
Andante ♪ = c. 112
42.
1
2
3
rall.
Allegretto ♩ = c. 92
43.

The Simple or Long Appoggiatura

Andante con spirito ♩ = c. 88

44.

p

crescendo poco a poco

f

p *sf* *sf*

1/2 1/2

f *p*

rall.

Allegro moderato ♩ = c. 104

45.

rall.

Andante con espressione ♩ = c. 72

46.

Allegro con spirito ♩ = c. 124
47.
1
2
1
2
The Short Appoggiatura
Allegro poco andantino ♩ = c. 100
48.
simile

Allegro moderato ♩. = c. 84
49.
1
2
3
Allegro moderato ♩ = c. 80
50.
3
3

Allegretto ♩ = c. 112
51.
Allegretto ♩ = c. 88
52.

Allegro moderato ♩ = c. 88
53.
Allegretto ♩ = c. 96
54.
The Portamento
Andante ♩ = c. 76
55.
Agitato
rall.
Tempo I

Andante ♩ = c. 88
56.
Fine
D.C.
Andante ♩ = c. 84
57.
Poco più mosso
rall.
Tempo I
Allegretto ♩ = c. 100
58.

Andante moderato ♩ = c. 84
59.
The Trill
♩ = c. 120 – 152 (60-67)
60.

61.
(one breath)
62.
(one breath)

63.
64.
(one breath)
65.

66.
67.

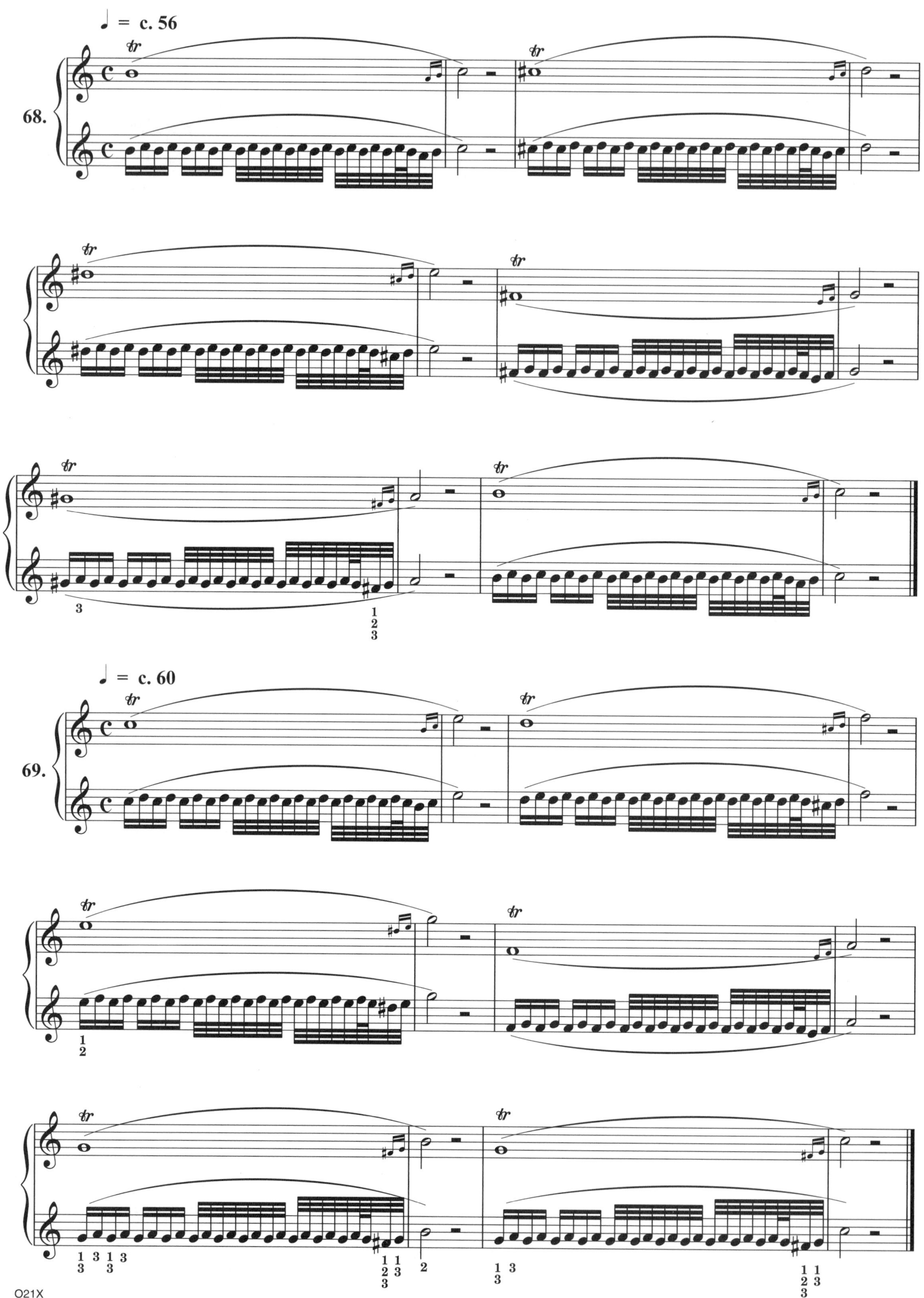
♩ = c. 56
68.
♩ = c. 60
69.

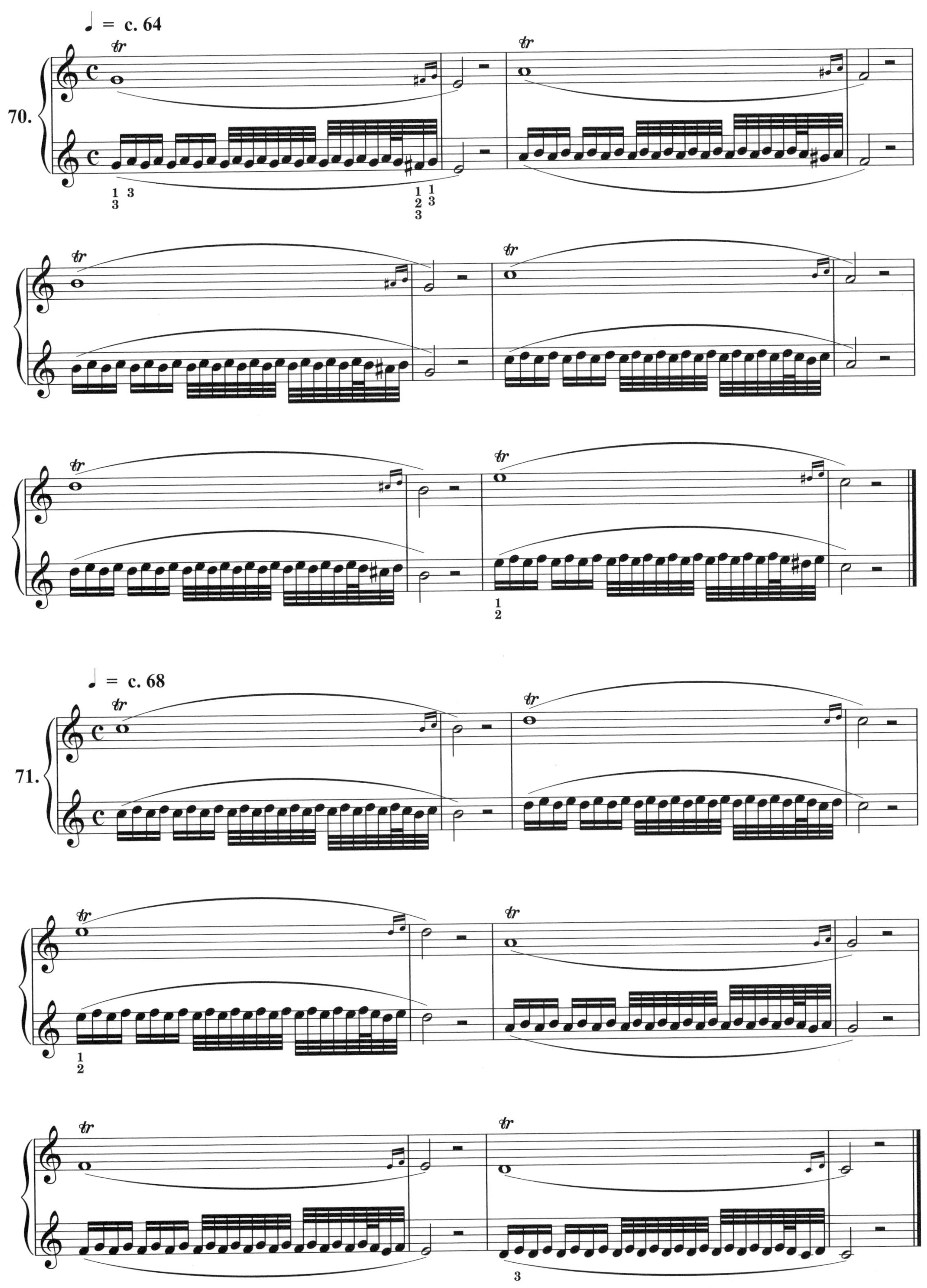

♩ = c. 64
70.
tr
♩ = c. 68
71.

♩ = c. 60
72.
♩ = c. 64
73.
Andante ♩ = c. 88
74.
mp
p
mp
mf
p
mf

Andante ♩ = c. 88
75.
poco cresc.
Andantino ♪ = c. 120
76.
Poco piú mosso
cresc.
dim. e rall.
Tempo I
rall.

Allegretto ♩ = c. 100
77.
rall.
Tempo I
rall.
♩ = c. 104
78.
♩ = c. 108
79.

tr
♩ = c. 100
80.
1
2
3

The Mordent

Allegro moderato ♩ = c. 96
83.
Fine
D.C.
Allegro ♩ = c. 100 – 120
84.
Fine
D.C.

Allegro ♩ = c. 116
85.
Allegretto ♩. = c. 92
86.
Allegretto ♩. = c. 88
87.

1
2
3
Allegretto ♩. = c. 92 – 116
88.
Fine
D.C.

V. More Advanced Studies

Intervals

The studies on intervals should be practiced diligently. Be careful not to change the position of the mouthpiece when moving from a low to a high note or from a high to a low note. By observing this rule, the player will acquire greater precision in attack and facility in playing (see Studies nos. 1–7).

Broken Octaves and Tenths

Broken octaves and tenths are not frequently used in music for the cornet or trumpet; nevertheless, octaves can be very effective when sensibly employed. This also applies to tenths. It would be very difficult to play in quick tempo any melody employing consecutive tenths (see Studies nos. 8–12).

Triplets 

The use of triplets is always highly effective. In order to play triplets well, each note must be articulated as evenly as possible. Practice slowly at first and do not increase the tempo until you have mastered the regular movement of the fingers (see Studies nos. 13–27).

Rhythmic figure

For a faultless performance of sixteenth notes, practice these studies carefully, always maintaining a steady beat and observing the indicated articulations in strict time. Practice slowly at first and gradually increase the tempo as you become familiar with the study. Too fast a tempo does not always give the performance the brilliance expected. Precision and evenness of tone are the true basis for fine playing (see Studies nos. 28–47).

Major and Minor Arpeggios

Many studies on major and minor arpeggios have been provided so that the student will be able to play easily in all of the keys. Some fingerings present difficulties at first glance, but do not avoid them for this reason. On the contrary, approach them with conviction. Some benefit will always be gained from trying them, even when the arpeggios are played very slowly.

The effort made to overcome certain technical "impossibilities" will quickly prove that these difficulties only appeared to be impossible (see Studies nos. 48–52).

The Dominant Seventh Arpeggio

The dominant seventh chord is the same in both the major and minor modes for each key. Studies on the dominant seventh arpeggio will complement the preceding studies. Practice the dominant seventh arpeggio carefully, maintaining the same evenness recommended throughout this method (see Studies nos. 53–54).

The Diminished Seventh Arpeggio

The diminished seventh chord plays a prominent role in modern musical composition. An extremely useful chord because of its flexible nature, it is made up exclusively of minor thirds and can be interpreted in many different ways. Normally, however, it is found in the minor scale, and its most common use can be seen in Study no. 55.

Diminished seventh chords are easily linked together and sequences of these chords are acceptable writing practice. Many varied rhythmic patterns and harmonic progressions using the diminished seventh are presented in the studies so that the students may become fully familiar with the chord and its usage (see Studies nos. 55–61).

Cadenzas

A series of cadenzas in the form of preludes have been added to the end of this section, so that the student may learn to end a solo effectively. Each cadenza should be transposed into all the keys. Be sure to take a breath properly whenever a rest occurs, so that the end of the phrase can be reached with full power and without allowing the pitch to drop out of tune. Otherwise, the effect will be completely destroyed.

Intervals*

* Refer to page 143.

** Practice in the following four ways: 1) single tongue

2) slur two notes up

3) slur two notes down

4) slur all in one breath

♩ = c. 56–108
2.
simile
simile
simile
simile
simile
simile
simile
simile
simile
simile

♩ = c. 52–88
3.
3 2 3 3
1 2

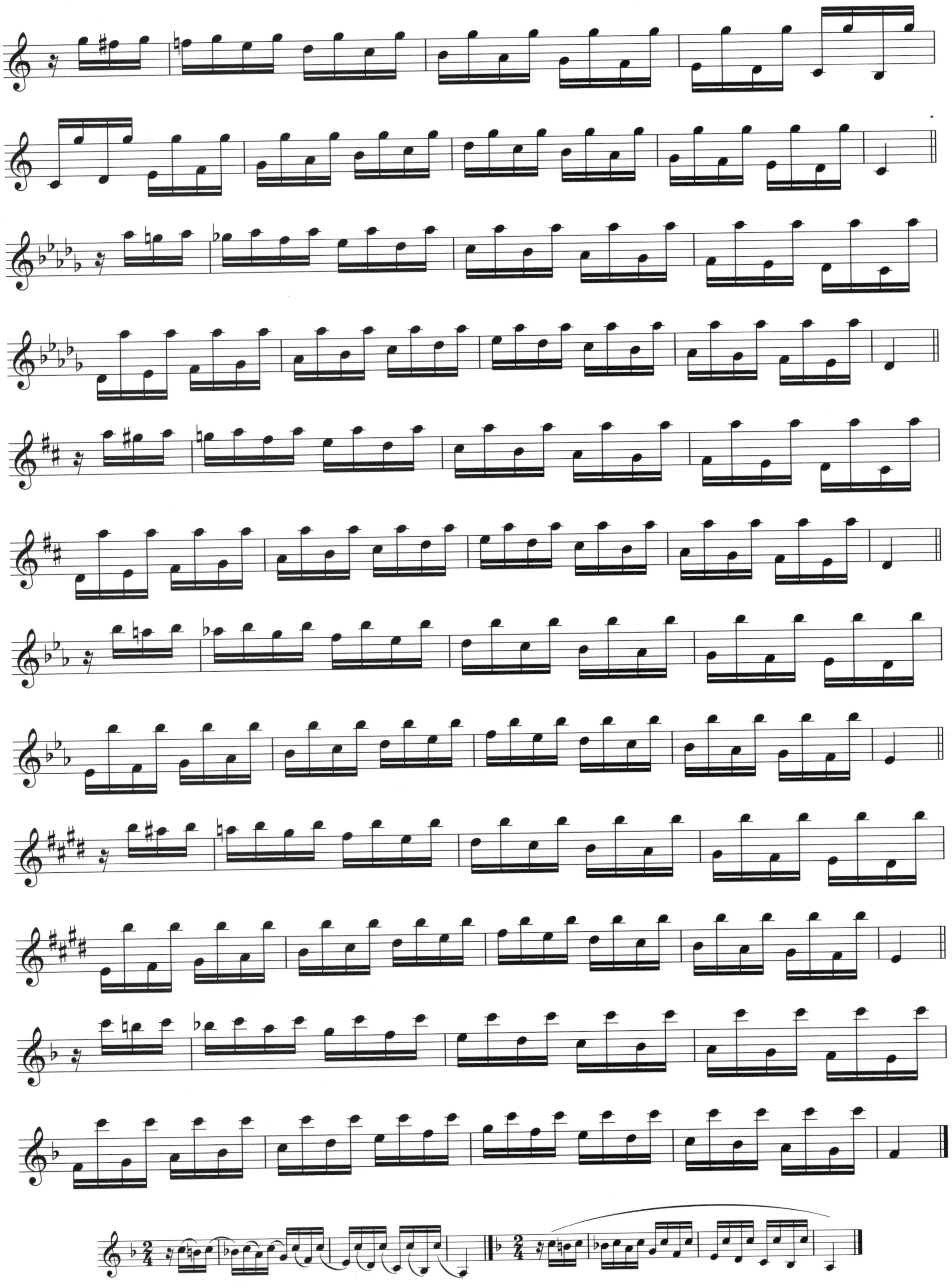

♩ = c. 52–80
4.
3
3

♩ = c. 52–80
5.

♩ = c. 48–80
6.

7.
No. 6.
No. 7.

Broken Octaves and Tenths*

* Refer to page 143.

Triplets*

*Play as much on one breath as possible. After the proper speed is reached, try to play each triplet exercise on one breath. * Refer to page 143.

♩ = c. 92 – (14-19)
14.
15.
3
3
3

16.
17.

18.
19.

𝅗𝅥 = c. 96–
20.
3
♩ = c. 100–
21.
1
2

♩ = c. 100–
22.
3
𝅗𝅥 = c. 100 (23–27)
23.
24.

25.
26.
simile
27.

Rhythmic Figure  *

♩ = c. 112 – 136 (28-38)

28.

29.

30.

3

simile

3

* Refer to page 143.

1
2

31.
32.

33.
34.
35.
1
2
1
2
1
2
1
2

36.
37.

38.
♩ = c. 96–136 (39-45)
39.

40.
41.
1
2
42.

43.
44.
45.

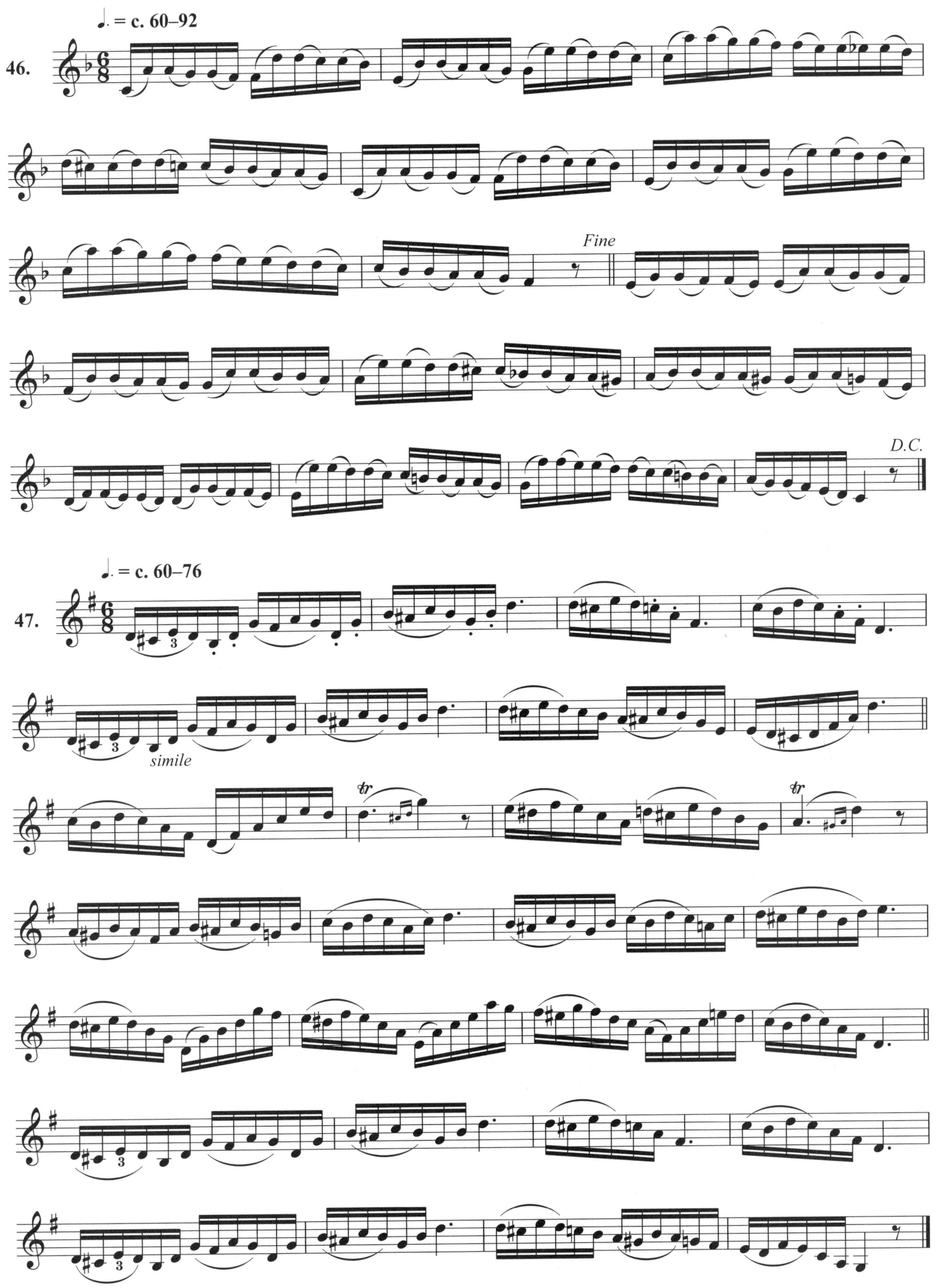
♩. = c. 60–92
46.
Fine
D.C.
♩. = c. 60–76
47.
3
simile
tr

Major and Minor Arpeggios*

Major Arpeggios

♩. = c. 84 –

48.

* Refer to page 143.

Minor Arpeggios

Major Arpeggios

Minor Arpeggios
♩ = c. 96 –
51.

Major Arpeggios

Dominant Seventh Arpeggios*

* Refer to page 143.

♩ = c. 116 –
54.

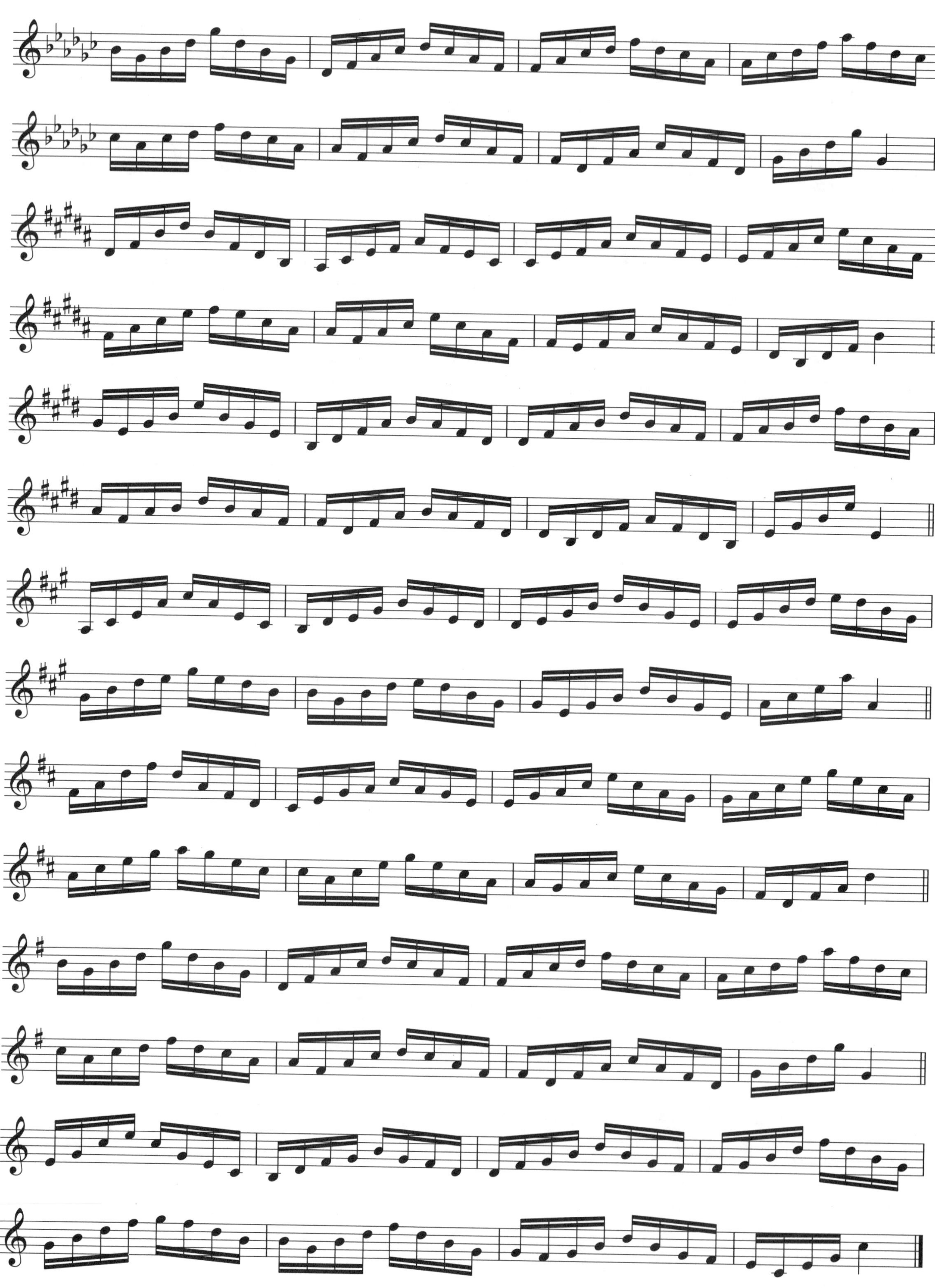

Diminished Seventh Arpeggios*

♩ = c. 112 –

55.

* Refer to page 143.

♩. = c. 92 – Play nos. 56-61 as much as possible on one breath.
56.
♩ = c. 128 –
57.

♩ = c. 128 –
58.
♩ = c. 96 –
59.

♩ = c. 96 –
60.
♩ = c. 96 –
61.

Cadenzas*

62.

a piacere

* Refer to page 143.

VI. Tonguing

Triple Tonguing

This staccato effect consists of playing detached and evenly without allowing the tonguing to become either too short or too long. In order to master triple tonguing, the earlier studies, which serve as a basis for this, should be practiced very slowly.

First, the student should try to pronounce with perfect evenness the syllables:

For greater evenness in tonguing, it is necessary at first to prolong each syllable a little. When greater precision in tonguing has been achieved, the syllables should then be shortened in order to produce the true staccato.[24]

The mechanics of tonguing in triple staccato, or triple tonguing, can be easily described in the following manner:

In pronouncing the syllables "tu, tu," the tongue is placed against the upper teeth and then drawn away, thus producing the first two sounds. In pronouncing the syllable "ku," the tongue is raised to the roof of the mouth to obstruct the throat and is then drawn away again. This allows a column of air to enter the mouthpiece, thus producing the third sound.[25]

In order to achieve a perfectly even to-and-fro movement of the tongue, practice slowly so that the tongue, like a valve, may allow the same quantity of air to escape for each syllable. By using this type of articulation, no passage will be too difficult and tone production on the cornet will be as easy as on the flute. To achieve this, however, the pronunciation must be perfectly clean and clear. Experience has shown that, for a really good playing technique, the syllables must be pronounced "tu-tu-ku, tu-tu-ku, tu" as indicated above, and not du-du-gu, du-du-gu, du." The latter, it is true, are quicker, but instead of detaching and detailing the sound, they slur it together.[26]

The tonguing should not be rushed, so that the listener is no longer able to distinguish it; sufficient speed may be obtained by using the method indicated above. The most important points to master are clarity and evenness (see Studies nos. 1-76).

24 As Arban states, it is beneficial to practice triple tonguing slowly with a prolonged syllable. To clarify, the syllable that is prolonged is the vowel following the initial strike of the tongue. No matter how fast or short your multiple tonguing is, maintaining consistent air flow will help the tongue to stay relaxed and flexible. (Hooten/Marotta)

25 The translation of Arban's "tu" can often be misunderstood. The French pronunciation of "tu ku" translates closer in English to "tee kee." The "ee" pronunciation requires the tongue to be in a higher and more forward position than the "u" vowel sound. However, when forming the "ee" syllable, be sure not to pull the tongue too far back in the mouth, which causes the position to be too high in the mouth. When practicing to find the optimum tongue position for each individual, practice with very small incremental change.

This may help in understanding the actual syllable; however, it is even more important to understand that this syllable is more of an imitation of the sound of an energized air stream, as opposed to a vocal pronunciation of the syllable without the follow through of air. It's important to remember that when experimenting with physical changes, one must make sure to keep an ear on the result. (Hooten/Marotta)

26 A common practice today when multiple tonguing is to keep the notes open-ended. The "t" or "k" acts as a clarifier within a constant air stream, without stopping the flow. This way of multiple tonguing can be used as a default, and the player can adjust the length as needed, depending on the piece and style. (Hooten/Marotta)

Double Tonguing

This type of staccato effect is extremely useful for playing scales and arpeggios in duple rhythm. In order to achieve precise playing, practice slowly following the same guidelines stated for triple-tonguing. First of all pronounce the syllables:

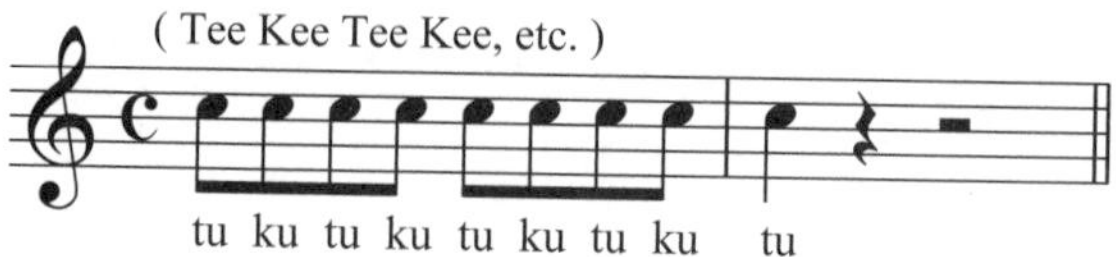

From this, it can be seen that the tongue performs a to-and-fro movement, which is very difficult to do with perfect evenness. However, once this movement is mastered, the most difficult passages may be played with all the speed, energy and strength desired.

After practicing all the studies on double-tonguing, the student should review the studies on scales, major and minor arpeggios, the dominant seventh arpeggio and the diminished seventh arpeggio, using double-tonguing. This will accustom the fingers to play in synchronization with the tongue and will be very beneficial in the end (see Studies nos. 77–114).

The Slur and Double Tonguing

In order to combine slurring with double tonguing, a special type of pronunciation must be used. The constant use of staccato tonguing without the occasional use of slurs becomes monotonous. Their combined use results in a pleasing variety of playing, which also facilitates a faster tempo.

This articulation is achieved by pronouncing the following syllables:

The syllable "ta-a" serves to attack the first note, and the syllable "a" which follows, enables the player, by prolonging the sound, to slur easily to the second note. This type of tonguing is indispensable and is used in all types of music (see Studies nos. 114–134).[27]

Fanfare Tonguing

Many students, both the conservatory and elsewhere, who were able to play the fanfare tonguing on the trumpet, scarcely ever succeeded in playing the true staccato correctly. From this observation, one may conclude that this type of tonguing is an obstacle to playing other types of articulations. Therefore, its practice is not advisable until the student has thoroughly mastered the other types. Moreover, fanfare tonguing is extremely easy to play once the student is able to perform the double and triple tonguing fluently (see Studies nos. 135–143).[28]

27 When one applies the syllables from footnote no. 26, it is not necessary to adjust to a different syllable when adding slurs to tongued passages. (Hooten/Marotta)

28 Arban is encouraging the player to develop a good fundamental base of multiple tonguing before limiting their abilities to only short, quick bursts. When one masters the endurance of good technique, the shorter bursts will come easily. (Hooten/Marotta)

Triple Tonguing*

* The player is encouraged to transpose these studies to various other keys.* Refer to page 188.

𝅗𝅥 = c. 68–128 (6–17)
6.
tu tu ku tu tu ku tu tu ku tu
7.
tu tu ku tu tu ku tu tu ku tu
8.
tu tu ku tu tu ku tu tu ku tu
9.
tu tu ku tu tu ku tu tu ku tu tu ku tu

10.
tu tu ku tu tu ku tu tu ku tu tu ku tu
11.
tu tu ku tu tu ku tu tu ku tu tu ku tu

12.
tu tu ku tu tu ku tu tu ku tu
13.
tu tu ku tu tu ku tu tu ku tu
14.

15.
tu tu ku tu tu ku tu tu ku tu tu ku tu tu ku tu tu ku tu
simile
16.
tu tu ku tu tu ku tu tu ku tu tu ku tu
simile
17.
tu tu ku tu tu ku tu tu ku tu tu ku tu
simile

♩. = c. 140–
18.
tu tu ku tu tu ku tu tu ku tu
simile
♩. = c. 144–
19.
tu tu ku tu tu ku tu tu ku tu
simile
𝅗𝅥 = c. 76–124 (20–22)
20.
tu tu ku tu tu ku tu tu ku tu tu ku tu
simile
21.
tu tu ku tu tu ku tu tu ku tu tu ku tu
simile

22.
tu tu ku tu tu ku tu tu ku tu tu ku tu
simile
23.
𝅗𝅥 = c. 76–
tu tu ku tu tu ku tu tu ku tu tu ku tu
simile
24.
𝅗𝅥 = c. 72 –
25.
♩ = c. 148 – 𝅗𝅥 = c. 84

Theme
♩ = c. 64
26.
♩. = c. 60
27.
tu tu ku tu tu ku tu
♩. = c. 60
28.
tu tu ku tu tu ku tu

♩ = c. 116
29.
tu tu ku tu tu ku tu tu ku tu tu ku tu
simile
♩ = c. 116
30.
tu tu ku tu tu ku tu tu ku tu tu ku tu
♩ = c. 116
31.
tu tu ku tu tu ku tu tu ku tu tu ku tu
𝅗𝅥 = 92
32.
tu tu ku tu tu ku tu
simile

𝅗𝅥 = c. 76–100
33.
3
3
3
3
tu tu ku tu tu ku tu
♩ = 76–108
34.
6
3
3
6
3
3
tu tu ku tu tu ku tu tu ku tu tu ku tu
simile
♩ = 76–108
35.
6
3
3
6
3
3
tu tu ku tu tu ku tu tu ku tu tu ku tu

36.
𝅗𝅥 = 68–
tu tu ku tu tu ku tu tu ku tu tu ku
37.
Theme
♩ = c. 68

♩ = c. 76–108
38.
♩ = c. 76–108 (39–41)
39.
40.
simile

41.
Theme
♩ = c. 64
42.
♩ = c. 84–108 (43–46)
simile
43.

44.
3
3
3
3
3
3
3
3
45.
3
3
3
3
3
3
3
3
simile
46.
3
3
3
3
3
3
3
3

♩= c. 80–124 (47–56)
47.
tu tu ku tu tu ku tu
simile
simile
48.
tu tu ku tu tu ku tu
simile
49.
tu tu ku tu tu ku tu
simile
50.
tu tu ku tu tu ku tu
simile

51.
simile
52.
tu tu ku tu tu ku tu
simile
53.
tu tu ku tu tu ku tu tu ku tu
simile
54.
simile
55.
simile

56.
simile
♩ = c. 80–124 (57–62)
57.
tu tu ku tu tu ku tu tu ku tu tu ku tu tu tu ku tu tu ku tu tu ku
simile
58.
tu tu ku tu tu ku tu tu ku tu tu ku
simile
59.
tu tu ku tu tu ku tu tu ku tu tu ku
simile

60.
3
3
3
3
simile
61.
3
3
3
3
3
simile
3 1 3
3
3 1 3
3

62.
3
3
3
3
simile
simile
♩ = c. 80 (63–69)
63.
3
3
3
3
simile
64.
3
3
3
3
simile

65.
simile
66.
simile
67.
tu ku tu tu ku tu tu ku tu tu ku tu

68.
69.
Presto ♩ = c. 112–180
70.
1.
2.

♩ = c. 80–124 (71–73)
71.
tu tu ku tu
tu tu ku tu
tu tu tu ku tu tu ku tu tu ku tu tu tu ku tu tu ku tu tu ku tu
1
2
tu ku tu
72.
3
73.

Theme
♩ = c. 84
74.
mf
fz
tr
♩ = c. 112
VAR.
Fine
D.S. al fine

Theme
Andantino ♩ = c. 72
75.
♩ = c. 80
VAR.
6
6
6

For He's a Jolly Good Fellow

Double Tonguing*

* The player is encouraged to transpose these studies to various other keys.* Refer to page 188.

82.
tu ku tu ku tu ku tu
83.
tu ku tu ku tu ku tu ku tu ku tu ku tu
84.
tu ku tu ku tu ku tu ku tu ku tu ku tu
85.
tu ku tu ku tu ku tu ku tu ku tu ku tu
86.

87.
tu ku tu ku tu
simile
88.
tu ku tu ku tu ku tu ku tu
simile
89.
tu ku tu ku tu ku tu ku tu ku tu ku tu
simile
90.
tu ku tu ku tu ku tu ku tu ku tu ku tu ku tu ku tu
simile
simile

♩ = c. 68–116
91.
tu ku tu ku tu ku tu ku tu ku tu ku
♩ = c. 72–120
92.
tu ku tu ku tu ku tu ku tu ku tu ku
♩ = c. 96–140
93.
tu ku tu ku tu ku tu ku tu

♩ = c. 92–136
94.
tu ku tu ku tu ku tu ku tu ku tu ku
♩ = c. 96–140 (95-97)
95.
ku tu ku tu ku tu ku tu ku tu ku tu ku tu ku tu ku tu
1
2
1
2
96.
ku tu ku tu ku tu ku tu
3
97.
ku tu ku tu ku tu ku tu ku tu ku tu ku tu

♩ = c. 116–160 (98–102)
98.
tu ku tu ku tu
99.
tu ku tu ku tu ku tu ku tu
100.
tu ku tu ku tu ku tu ku tu ku tu ku tu ku tu ku tu
101.
tu tu ku tu ku tu ku tu ku tu ku tu
102.
tu tu ku tu ku tu ku tu

♩ = c. 96–136
103.
tu ku tu ku tu ku tu ku tu ku tu ku tu tu ku tu ku tu ku tu
tu ku tu ku tu
ku tu ku tu
♩ = c. 92–120
104.
3 ku tu ku tu ku tu ku tu ku tu
3 3 3
ku tu ku tu ku
tu ku tu ku tu tu ku tu ku tu ku tu ku tu tu ku ku tu
3 ku tu ku tu ku tu ku tu ku tu ku tu ku
3 ku tu ku tu ku tu ku tu ku tu 3 ku tu ku tu ku tu ku tu ku tu
♩ = c. 116–136
105.
tu ku tu ku tu ku tu ku tu
Fine
tu tu ku tu tu ku tu
tu tu ku tu tu ku tu tu tu ku tu tu ku tu tu tu ku tu tu ku tu
D.C.
♩ = c. 104–128
106.
tu ku tu ku tu tu ku tu tu
Fine
tu ku tu ku tu ku tu
D.C.

♩ = c. 124–160
107.
tu ku tu ku tu ku tu ku tu ku tu ku tu
♩ = c. 108–136 (108–111)
108.
tu tu ku tu ku tu ku tu ku tu ku tu ku tu ku tu
109.
tu tu ku tu ku tu ku tu ku tu ku tu ku tu ku tu
110.
tu tu ku tu ku tu ku tu ku tu ku tu ku tu ku tu

111.
tu tu ku tu ku tu ku tu
♩ = c. 112–152 (112–114)
112.
tu ku tu ku tu ku tu ku tu
simile
simile
113.
tu ku tu ku tu ku tu ku tu

114.
tu ku tu ku tu ku tu ku tu ku tu ku tu ku tu ku tu ku tu ku tu
The Slur and Double Tonguing
♩ = c. 120–160 (115–118)
115.
ta - ta ka ta ta - ta ka ta
1
2
116.
ta - ta ka ta ta - ta ka ta
117.
ta - ta ka ta ka ta ka ta ta - ta ka ta ka ta ka ta

118.
ta - ta ka ta - ta ka ta - ta ka ta
♩ = c. 124–160 (119-122)
119.
ta - ta ka ta - ta ka ta - ta ka ta - ta ka ta - ta ka ta - ta ka ta
120.
ta - ta ka ta ka ta ka ta - ta ka ta ka ta ka ta
121.
ta - ta ka ta - ta ka ta - ta ka ta

122.
ta - ta ka ta - ta ka ta - ta ka
simile
simile
♩ = c. 116–140 (123–126)
123.
ta ka ta - ta ka ta - ta
simile
124.
ta ka ta - ta ka ta - ta ka ta - ta ka ta - ta

125.
ta ka ta - ta ka ta - ta ka ta - ta ka ta - ta
126.
ta - ta ka ta - ta ka ta - ta ka ta - ta ka
♩ = c. 120–140 (127–130)
127.
ta - ta ka ta - ta ka ta - ta ka ta - ta ka
128.
ta - ta ka ta - ta ka ta - ta ka ta - ta ka

129.
ta - ta ka ta - ta ka ta - ta ka ta - ta ka ta
130.
ta - ta ka ta - ta ka ta - ta ka ta - ta ka ta
Allegro ♩ = c. 128–160 (131–133)
131.
ta - ta ka ta ka ta ka ta - ta ka ta - ta ka ta

Allegro
132.
ta ka ta ka ta ka ta - ta ka ta - ta ka ta ka ta ka ta - ta ka ta - ta ka ta
Allegro
133.
ta - ta ka ta - ta ka ta
Presto ♩ = c. 140–172
134.
ta ta ka ta ta
ta - ta ka ta ka ta ka
ta - ta ka ta - ta ka ta - ta ka ta

Fanfare Tonguing*

* The player is encouraged to transpose these studies to various other keys.* Refer to page 188.

♩ = c. 108–120
138.
tu tu ku tu tu tu tu tu tu
tu tu ku tu tu tu
tu tu ku tu tu tu tu tu ku tu tu
Fine
D.C.
♩ = c. 112–124
139.
tu tu ku tu tu tu ku tu
tu tu ku tu tu tu ku tu
tu tu ku
tu tu ku
tu
tu tu ku tu
♩ = c. 124–136
140.
tu tu ku tu
tu tu ku tu
tu tu ku tu
mf
f
f
Fine
mf
f
D.C.
♩ = c. 116
141.
tu ku tu ku tu
tu ku tu ku tu

♩. = c. 96
142.
tu tu ku tu ku tu
♩. = c. 104
143.
tu ku tu ku tu
♩ = c. 96
144.
3
3
tu tu ku tu tu tu
♩ = c. 100
145.
3
tu tu ku tu tu tu
tu tu ku tu tu ku
tu tu ku tu tu tu
tu tu ku tu tu ku tu tu ku tu tu ku
tu tu ku tu
tu tu ku tu tu ku tu

VII. The Art of Phrasing
150 Classic and Popular Melodies
Arranged by Jean-Baptiste Arban

How Fair Thou Art
H. WEIDT
Moderato
4.
p
cresc.
ff
America
(My Country, 'Tis of Thee)
Andante maestoso
5.
p ben sostenuto
f
Last Rose of Summer
Larghetto
6.
p
f
a tempo
p
f
My Own, My Guiding Star
Robin Hood
Andante cantabile
7.
p
rit.
a tempo
f

Why Do I Weep for Thee?
Andante con tristesso
WILLIAM VINCENT WALLACE
8.
p dolce
cresc.
pp
rall.
Blue Bells of Scotland
Allegro moderato
9.
f
Dutch Air
Maestoso
10.
f

Now the Swallows Are Returning
FRANZ ABT
Andantino
11.
p dolce
rall.
Who Shall Be Fairest?
Andante
12.
p
mf
rall.
a tempo
ff
Russian Hymn
Maestoso
13.
ff
p
cresc.

O, Ye Tears
Andante
FRANZ ABT
14.
p
con espress.
accel.
rit.
rit.
Puritan's Daughter
Larghetto cantabile
MICHAEL WILLIAM BALFE
15.
p
3
3
3
3
Woodman Spare That Tree
Andante
HENRY RUSSELL
16.
p
3

Love Not
V. WALLACE
Cantabile
17.
p
cresc.
p
p dolce
rit.
espress.
p
cresc.
Then You'll Remember Me
MICHAEL WILLIAM BALFE
Andante
18.
p dolce
f
O Wert Thou but Mine Own Love
FRIEDRICH WILHELM KÜCKEN
Andante
19.
p
mf
rall.

We May Be Happy Yet
Andante moderato
MICHAEL WILLIAM BALFE
20.
p
rall.
cresc.
Constance
Andante espressione
G. LINLEY
21.
p
rall.
a tempo
The Heart of Thy Nora Is Breaking for Thee
Andantino
G. LINLEY
22.
p
rall.
a tempo
3
3

Il poliuto
(Excerpt)

GAETANO DONIZETTI

Larghetto

23.

p

p

calando

The Heart Bowed Down

MICHAEL WILLIAM BALFE

Larghetto cantabile

24.

p

p

When We Meet Again

L. WALDMANN

Moderato

25.

p dolce

f

p

German Song

Andante moderato

26.

p *mf* *f* *p* *rall.*

Friends of My Youth

Andante

GEORGE BARKER

27.

p *cresc.* *p* *f* *p* *ad lib.*

Romance

from *Fleur de Thé*

Andantino ma non lento (♪)

CHARLES LECOCQ

28.

p

Poco animato

rall. *a tempo* *rit.*

Poco più lento
Animato
rall.
There Is a Flower That Bloometh
V. WALLACE
Moderato
29.
p
L'ara o l'avello apprestami
GIUSEPPE VERDI
Moderato
30.
p
3
3
Più mosso

My Bark Which o'er the Tide
Allegretto
MICHAEL WILLIAM BALFE
31.
p
'Twas Rank and Fame
Andante cantabile
MICHAEL WILLIAM BALFE
32.
mf
rit. a piacere
Vien, Leonora
Larghetto
GAETANO DONIZETTI
33.
p

Les vêpres siciliennes
(Excerpt)
GIUSEPPE VERDI
Largo cantabile
34.
mf
Black-Eyed Susan
Andante
35.
p

I'm Leaving Thee in Sorrow
Andante
G. BARKER
36.
p
f
p
Good-Bye, Sweetheart
Andante con moto
JOHN LIPTROT HATTON
37.
p
cresc.
string.
rall.
f

Farewell To Thee, Mary
F.N. GROUCH
Andante
38.
p
In Happy Moments
WILLIAM VINCENT WALLACE
Moderato
39.
p
Call Me Thine Own
F. HALEVY
Andantino espressivo
40.
p

Kathleen Mavourneen

Slumber On

Brightest Eyes

GIORGIO STIGELLI

Love's Own Tear

(Ballad)

T. CRAMPTON

Andante

44.

p dolce

p

cresc.

cresc.

p

p

dolce

sf

rall.

p

cresc.

Restore Those Visions Bright

Il furioso

Romance

Romanzetta
VINCENZO BELLINI
Andante cantabile
48.
p dolce
rall.
cresc.
f
rit.
Be Still, My Heart
PAUL HENRION
Andante
49.
p
Animato
rall.
a tempo
cresc.

Jessie
Andante
G. LINLEY
50.
p
rall.
a tempo
rall.
a tempo
Pieta rispetto
from Macbeth
Andante
GIUSEPPE VERDI
51.
p
f
f
rit.
The Exile's Lament
Con espressione
RICH ALBERT
52.
p
dolce

rall.
a tempo
agitato
rall.
a tempo
rall.
Les vêpres siciliennes
(Excerpt)
GIUSEPPE VERDI
Allegro agitato espressione
53.
dim.
dim.
I Think of Thee
FRANZ ABT
Andantino
54.
poco riten.
string.
rit.

poco riten.
string.
rit.
Beatrice di Tenda
Andante amoroso
(Excerpt)
VINCENZO BELLINI
55.
p con abbardono
a tempo
a piacere
Poco più lento
a piacere
La straniera
Moderato
(Excerpt)
VINCENZO BELLINI
56.
rall.
a tempo

Gemma di vergy
(Excerpt)
GAETANO DONIZETTI
Andante
57.
cresc.
cresc.
La gazza ladra
(Excerpt)
GIOACHINO ROSSINI
Andante con brio
58.
Fine
D.S.

La gazza ladra

(Excerpt)

GIOACHINO ROSSINI

59. **Allegro**

mf *grazioso* *f*

La donna del lago

(Excerpt)

GIOACHINO ROSSINI

60. **Allegro**

p *f* *leggiero* *f* *p*

La Cenerentola
(Excerpt)
GIOACHINO ROSSINI
Moderato
61.
Quando le sere al placido
(from Luisa Miller)
GIUSEPPE VERDI
Andante
62.
Alla vita che t'arride
(from Un ballo in maschera)
GIUSEPPE VERDI
Andante
63.

Presto
Cadenza ad lib.
The Irish Emigrant
Andante
G. BARKER
64.
p
rall.
a tempo
rall.
a tempo
cresc.
rit.
a tempo
p
cresc.
rall.

Don Giovanni
(Excerpt)
WOLFGANG AMADEUS MOZART
Andante
65.
p
rall.
Can I Be Dreaming?
from The Talisman
MICHAEL WILLIAM BALFE
Larghetto
66.
p dolce
fz

Le Désir
Moderato
LUDWIG VAN BEETHOVEN
67.
p
mf
p
Andante
(from Symphony No. 4 "Italian")
Andante con moto
FELIX MENDELSSOHN
68.
f
p
1.
2.
p
cresc.
sf
p
1.
2.
Al ben de'tuoi qual vittima
(from Lucia di Lammermoor)
Moderato
GAETANO DONIZETTI
69.
p

mf

Funeral March

FRÉDÉRIC CHOPIN

Lento

70.

p

cresc.

sf p

Anna Bolena

(Excerpt)

Moderato

GAETANO DONIZETTI

71.

mf *sf* *cresc.* *cresc.*

Anna Bolena

(Excerpt)

Cantabile

GAETANO DONIZETTI

72.

p *cresc.* *f* *rit.* *p* *sf* *sf* *p* *f* *ad lib.*

Ariette
Andante con moto
CARL MARIA von WEBER
73.
p
mf
Song of the Mermaids
Andante con moto
CARL MARIA von WEBER
74.
p dolce
p
rall.

L'amor funesto

Romeo
Andante
VINCENZO BELLINI
77.
p
f
dim.
f
f
dim.
f
Der Freischütz
(Excerpt)
Adagio
CARL MARIA von WEBER
78.
f
f
f
f
cresc.
f
Fine
D.S.

Adieu
Andante
FRANZ SCHUBERT
79.
con espressione
p
cresc.
f
Eulogy of Tears
Andante
FRANZ SCHUBERT
80.
f
3
dim.
cresc.
Anna Bolena
(Excerpt)
Larghetto
GAETANO DONIZETTI
81.
3

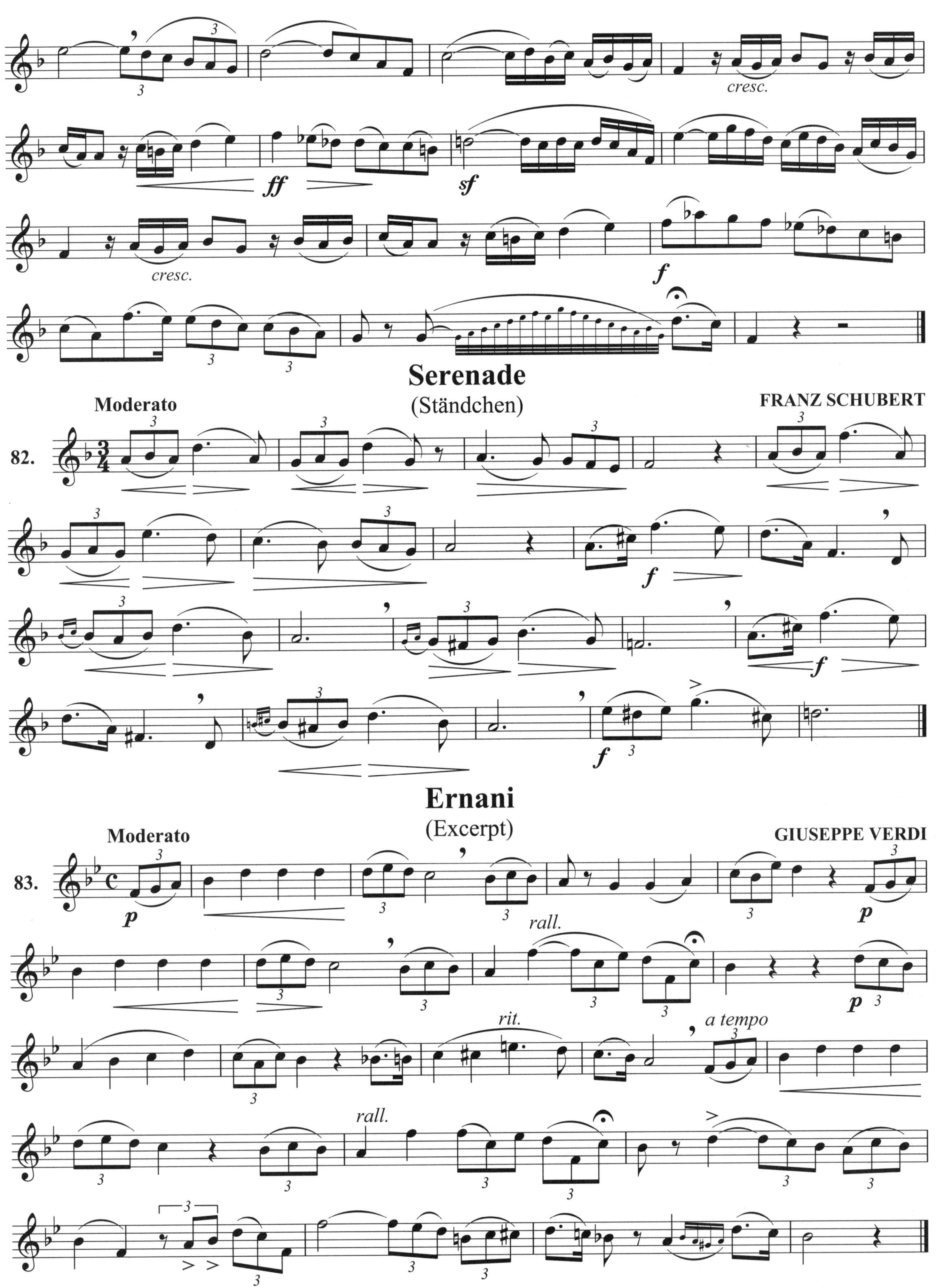

cresc.
ff
sf
cresc.
f
Serenade
(Ständchen)
Moderato
FRANZ SCHUBERT
82.
f
f
f
Ernani
(Excerpt)
Moderato
GIUSEPPE VERDI
83.
p
p
rall.
p
rit.
a tempo
rall.

Ernani
(Excerpt)
GIUSEPPE VERDI
Andante
84.
p
f
allarg.
allarg.
f
f
con espressione
L'Adieu
Andantino
85.
p dolce
f
p
cresc.
f
p
cresc.
f
p
f
rall.
p
dim.

Orange and Blue Jig
Allegro
86.
mf
Fine
f
D.S.
Lancashire Clog Dance
87.
mf
f
mf
Fine
mf
D.C.

L'amour

Andante
88.
p
f
p
p
f
p
f
pp
ad lib.
f
La Traviata
(Excerpt)
GIUSEPPE VERDI
Andante mosso
89.
p dolce
1.
2.
f
f
pp
mf
p
mf

La Traviata
(Excerpt)
GIUSEPPE VERDI
Allegro brillante
90.
mf
tr
f
3
La donna è mobile
(from Rigoletto)
GIUSEPPE VERDI
Allegretto
91.
f
p
a tempo
con forza

Rigoletto

(Excerpt)

GIUSEPPE VERDI

Il trovatore

(Excerpt)

GIUSEPPE VERDI

Il trovatore

(Excerpt)

GIUSEPPE VERDI

Andante

94.

p

p

p

Il trovatore

(Excerpt)

GIUSEPPE VERDI

Allegro

95.

f

f

Il trovatore
(Excerpt)
GIUSEPPE VERDI
Adagio
96.
p con espress.
rall.
a tempo
Il trovatore
(Excerpt)
GIUSEPPE VERDI
Allegro
97.
f
Agitato
p
rit.
a tempo
p

Il trovatore
(Excerpt)
GIUSEPPE VERDI
Allegretto
98.
Il trovatore
(Excerpt)
GIUSEPPE VERDI
Allegretto brillante
99.

Il trovatore
(Excerpt)
GIUSEPPE VERDI
Allegretto moderato
100.
f
rit.
a tempo
f
a tempo
O salutaris hostia
WOLFGANG AMADEUS MOZART
Adagio
101.
mf
f
f
p

Macbeth
(Excerpt)

GIUSEPPE VERDI

Allegretto maestoso

Le porte etendard

PETER JOSEPH von LINDPAINTNER

Serenade
Andantino
ANDRÉ MODESTE GRÈTRY
104.
p
poco cresc.
sf
sf
cresc.
mf
The Tear
Andante molto espressivo
KÜCKEN
105.
mf
f
p
f
f
dolce
rit.
dim.
dolce

Melody
FELIX MENDELSSOHN
Andantino
106.
p
rit.
La parisina
GAETANO DONIZETTI
Andante
107.
p dolce
rall.
a tempo
Norma
(Excerpt)
VINCENZO BELLINI
Allegretto moderato
108.
p
Lento
a tempo

O21X

Daughter of the Regiment
(Excerpt)
Andante con moto
GAETANO DONIZETTI
109.
p
Neapolitan Song
Andante animoto
110.
mf
ten.
men.
a piacere
3

La sonnambula
(Excerpt)
VINCENZO BELLINI
Andante
111.
I Capuletti
(Excerpt)
VINCENZO BELLINI
Allegretto maestoso
112.
Dopo due lustri
SAVERIO MERCADANTE
Andantino
113.
cresc.

Il crociato in Egitto

(Excerpt)

GIACOMO MEYERBEER

Andante quasi Allegretto

114.

dolce

Fine

mf

cresc. molto

p

f

D.S.

Euryanthe

(Excerpt)

CARL MARIA von WEBER

Andante con moto

115.

p

mf

p

Absence

LUDWIG VAN BEETHOVEN

Andantino

116.

p

rall.

a tempo

mf

rall.

The Captive

KÜCKEN

Lento con dolore

117.

f

ff *con espressione*

Otello

(Excerpt)

GIOACCHINO ROSSINI

Moderato

118.

p

dim.

f *dim.*

cresc.

dim. *f*

f *dim.*

Semiramide

(Excerpt)

Allegro

GIOACHINO ROSSINI

119.

L'elisire d'amore

(Excerpt)

Andante

GAETANO DONIZETTI

120.

Der Freischütz

(Excerpt)

CARL MARIA von WEBER

Il Trovatore

(Excerpt)

GIUSEPPE VERDI

Der Vogelfänger bin ich ja
(from The Magic Flute)
Allegretto
WOLFGANG AMADEUS MOZART
123.
mf
rall. poco a poco
a tempo
f
Niobe
(Excerpt)
Allegretto
GIOVANNI PACINI
124.
p
cresc.
f
mineur
f mineur
ad lib.

Swiss Song
Moderato
125.
p
f
f
La ci darem la mano
(from Don Giovanni)
WOLFGANG AMADEUS MOZART
Andante
126.
p
Fine
3
D.C.
Austrian National Hymn
FRANZ JOSEPH HAYDN
Maestoso
127.
p
f

O21X

La sonnambula
(Excerpt)
Allegro
VINCENZO BELLINI
128.
La parisina romanza
Moderato
GAETANO DONIZETTI
129.
rall.
a tempo

La sonnambula
(Excerpt)
VINCENZO BELLINI
Allegro moderato
130.
f
3
cresc.
cresc.
f
J'aimerai toute ma vie
DALAIRAC
Andantino
131.
p
p
sf
sf
f
cresc.
f
p
dim.
f
p
f
rall.
Neapolitan Song
Allegretto
132.
f
p
f
rit.
ten.
rit.
a tempo
f
p

rit.
a tempo
p
f
pp
rit.
Andante
(from Symphony No. 4 "Italian")
Adagio
FELIX MENDELSSOHN
133.
p
f
p
f
p
f
p
p
dim.
p
cresc.
f
p
Andante
The Alpine Horn
HEINRICH PROCH
134.
mf con espressione
f
cresc.
f
mf
f
p
f
p

La Traviata
(Excerpt)
GIUSEPPE VERDI
Allegretto con grazia
135.
rit.
a tempo
In mia man alfin tu sei
(from Norma)
VINCENZO BELLINI
Andante
136.

accel.
f
Il rival salvar tu dei
(from I puritani)
Lento
VINCENZO BELLINI
137.
p
mf
3

Thou Art So Near, and Yet So Far
ALEXANDER REICHARDT
Moderato
138.
mf con espress.
Più animato
rit.
a tempo
Più meno
When the Quiet Moon Is Beaming
JOHANNES SCHONDORF
Moderato
139.
dim.

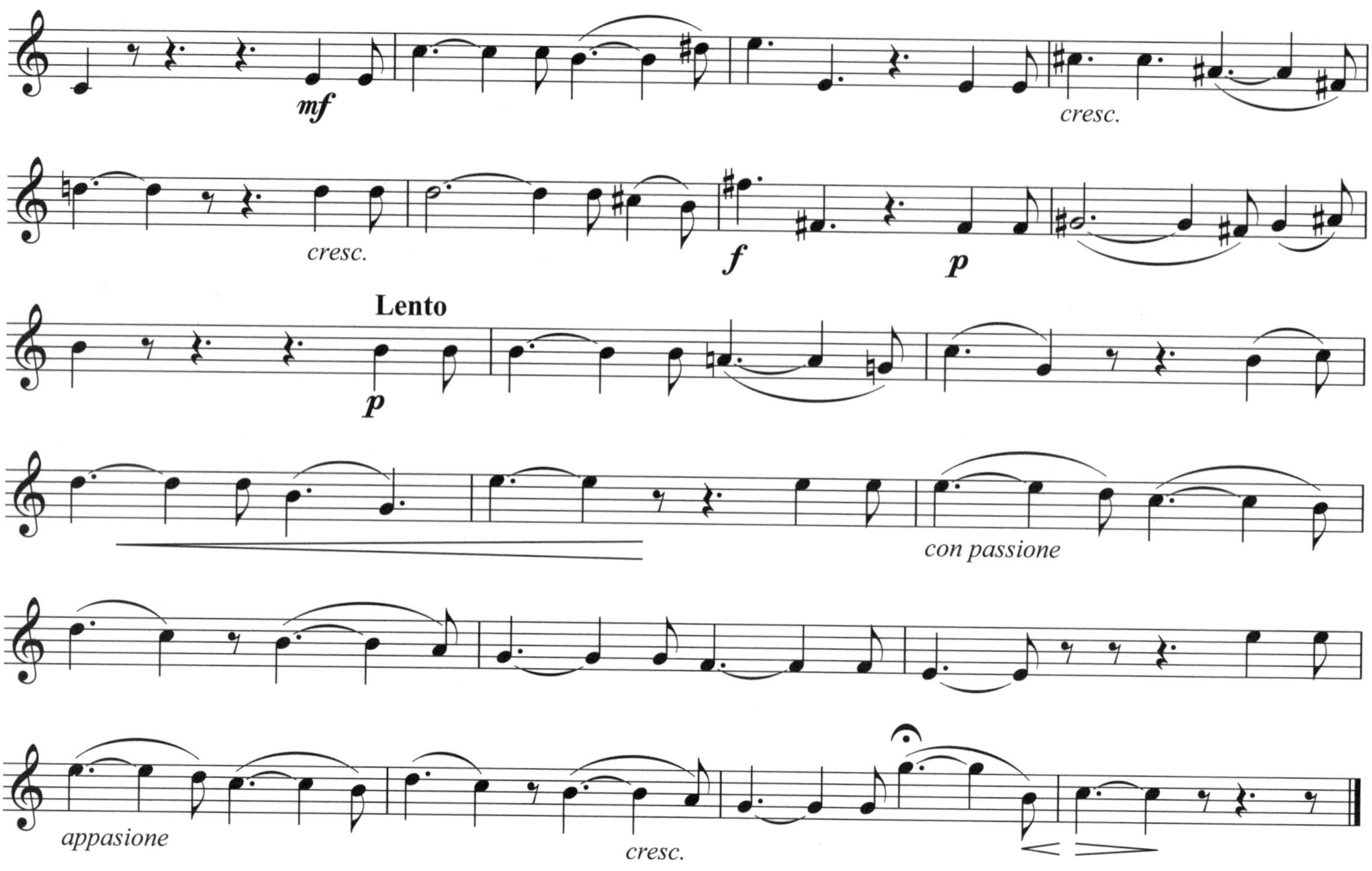

mf *cresc.*

cresc. *f* *p*

Lento

p

con passione

appasione *cresc.*

Cavatina

(from *Les Huguenots*)

Andantino **GIACOMO MEYERBEER**

140. *p*

cresc.

Bessonian Polka

141.

p

f

ff

1.

2.

p

To Coda

fz

p

ff

ff

1.

2.

p

Star of Paris Polka

Cavatina
(from *Ernani*)

GIUSEPPE VERDI

The Pilgrim of Love

Lento
p
rall.
Vivace
ff
Dear Little Heart
Moderato
145.
f
ad lib.
Theme
p con espress.
cresc.
Pno.

Var. I
mf
Pno.
Var. II
f
Pno.
Var. III
f
Più mosso
ff

Home, Sweet Home

SIR HENRY BISHOP

Var. II
f
Lento
p
a tempo
f
Più mosso
ff
Keel Row
Tempo di Marcia
147.
mf
f
Connected dah —>
Var. I
p
mf

Var. II
p
mf
Var. III
p
mf
Var. IV Tempo di Schott
mf
p
1.
Più mosso
2.
ff

Blue Bells of Scotland

Var. III
mf
Cadenza
Più mosso
ff
Yankee Doodle
Allegretto
149.
p
f
p
f
Var. I
mf

Var. II
f
America
(My Country, 'Tis of Thee)
Moderato
150.
p
f
ff
Var. I

Var. II
f
Var. III
Vivace
f

VIII. 68 Duets for Two Cornets

Melody
Moderato
Fine
4.
D.C.
Melody
Moderato
5.
Melody
SAVERIO
Moderato
6.

Adeste fideles
Andantino
JOHN FRANCIS WADE
7.
mf con espress.
mf con espress.
f
f
p
p
dolce
dolce
cresc.
cresc.
f
f
dim.
dim.
America
(My Country, 'Tis of Thee)
Andante
8.
mf
mf
f
f
Air
Allegretto poco Andante
WOLFGANG AMADEUS MOZART
9.
p con eleganza
p con eleganza

mf
mf
Air
Andante moderato un poco Allegretto
ANDRÉ GRÉTRY
10.
mf
mf
Fine
D.C.
Noel ancien
Moderato
11.
p semplice
p semplice

Andante con moto
Air
LUDWIG van BEETHOVEN
12.
p con eleganza
p
con eleganza
cresc.
dim.
dim.
Allegretto moderato
Arabian Song
13.
mf
mf
f
f

Serenade
Andantino
ANDRÉ GRÉTRY
14.
p dolce
p dolce
cresc.
cresc.
La romanesca
Allegretto
15.
p
mf
mf

Romance
(from *Joseph*)
Andante moderato
ÉTIENNE MÉHUL
16.
mf con espress.
mf con espress.
cresc.
mf
cresc.
mf
Romance
Andante sostenuto
JACQUES DE GOUY
17.
p
p
Fine
mf
mf
rall.
D.C.

Noel ancien

Allegretto
18.
p
mf
mf
March
JACQUES DE GOUY
Con energia
19.
ff
ff

Song of Master Adam

Allegretto moderato

JEAN BAPTISTE ARBAN

20.

Le souvenir

Andantino con moto

21.

Richard of the Lion Heart

ANDRÉ GRÉTRY

Silent Sorrow
Andante
SAMUEL WEBBE
24.
p
f
rall.
a tempo
dim.
Melody
Allegretto moderato
25.
mf

The Lion Hunt
SAVERIO
Allegretto
26.
mf
p
f

L'elisir d'amore
(Excerpt)
Lento
GAETANO DONIZETTI
27.
p
I Would That My Love
Moderato
FELIX MENDELSSOHN
28.
p
cresc.
f

Prayer to the Virgin

SAVERIO

March of Two Misers
Moderato
31.
Melody
Allegretto moderato
32.

Country Wedding
Allegro vivo
33.
mf
f

Bivouac Song

Allegro

34.

f

f

ff

ff

1. 2.

Birthday Festival

Moderato

35.

p

p

cresc.

cresc.

mf

mf

p

p

mf

f

mf

f

Melody
Allegretto
36.
p
p
mf
mf
German Song
KÜCKEN
Allegretto
37.
mf
mf

Richard of the Lion Heart
Andante cantabile
ANDRÉ GRÉTRY
38.
p dolce
p dolce
poco rit.
a tempo
mf
mf
p
March
Allegretto moderato
JACQUES DE GOUY
39.
p
p
f
p
f
p

Tic e Tic e Toc
Tempo di Valse
40.
Fine
1.
2.
D.C.

Carnival of Venice

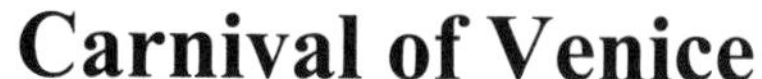

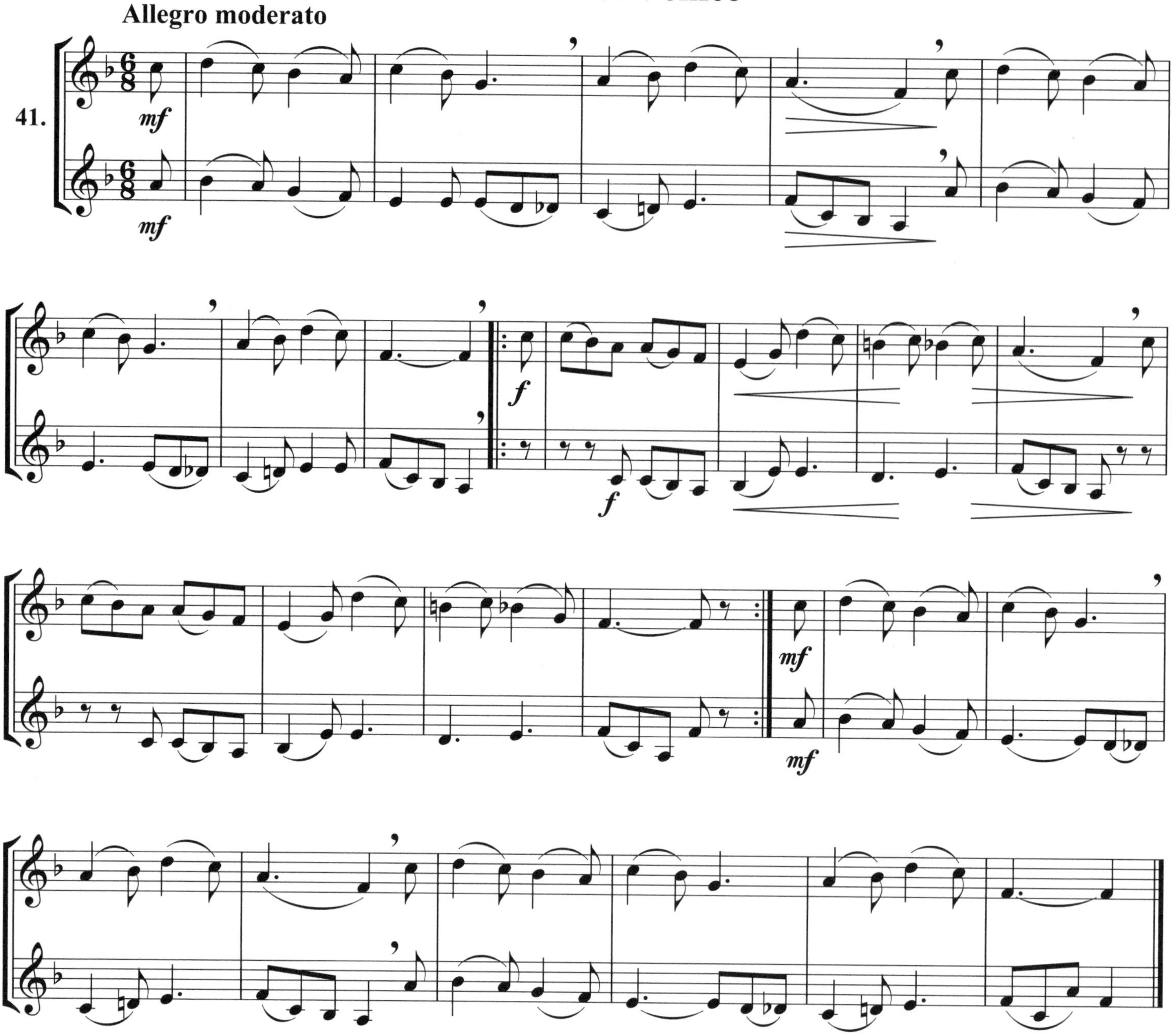
Allegro moderato
41.
mf
mf
f
f
mf
mf

Nel cor più

GIOVANNI PAISIELLO

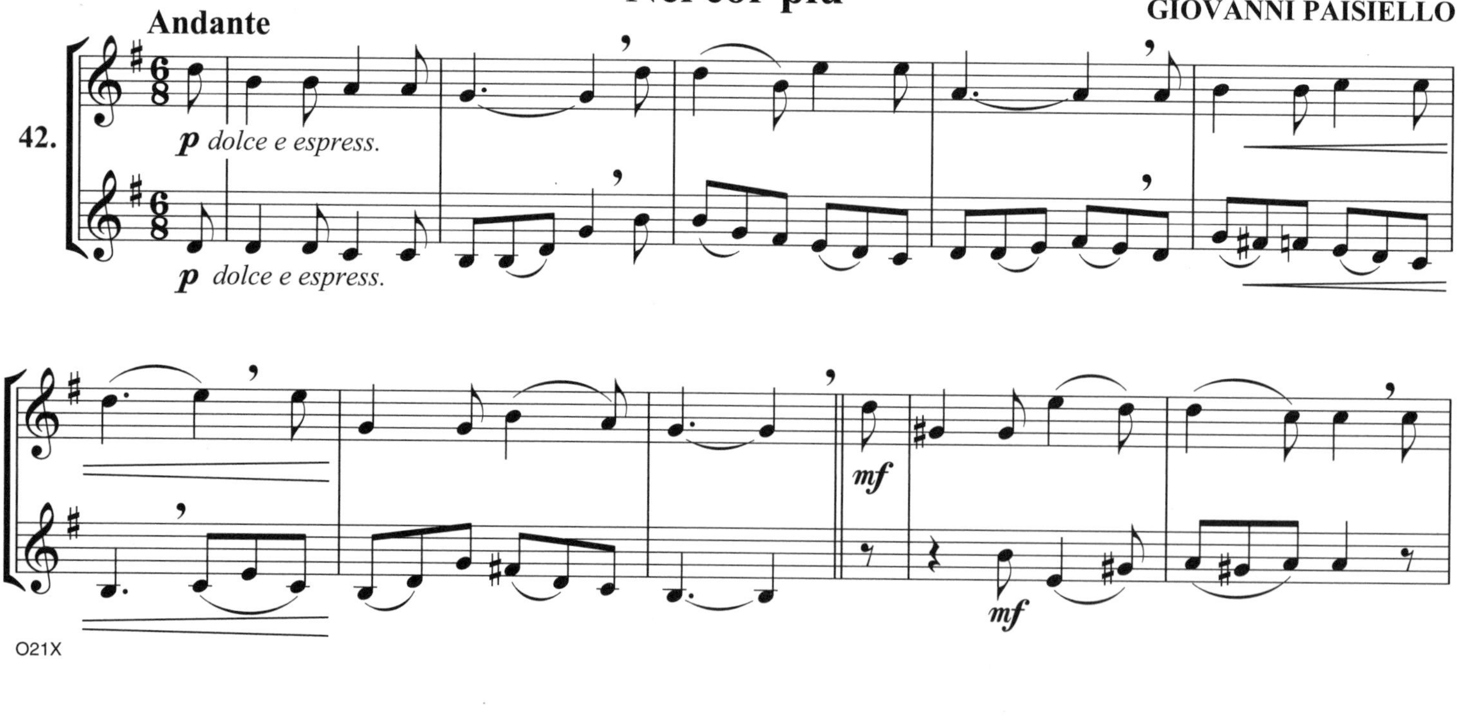
Andante
42.
p dolce e espress.
p dolce e espress.
mf
mf

Bolero
Lightly
JACQUES DE GOUY
43.
p
cresc.
mf
legato
f
ff

Norma
(Excerpt)

VINCENZO BELLINI

Last Rose of Summer

Andante sostenuto

46.

p

p

f

f

p

p

Evening Prayer

SAVERIO

Andante

47.

p grazioso

p

mf

mf

p

p

f

f

Cavatina

(from *La sonnambula*)

VINCENZO BELLINI

Andante moderato

48.

Austrian National Hymn

FRANZ JOSEPH HAYDN

Andante

49.

Der Freischütz
(Excerpt)
Allegro moderato
CARL MARIA von WEBER
50.
mf con espress.
mf con espress.
poco rit.
a tempo

French Air

Burning Fever

con molto dolce
con molto dolce
L'elisir d'amore
(Excerpt)
GAETANO DONIZETTI
Allegretto
53.
mf
mf
Fine
f
f

D.C.
Air
(from La sonnambula)
Allegro moderato
VINCENZO BELLINI
54.
f
rall.

Wind and Wave

Tyrolienne
Moderato
56.
p
p
mf
mf
Italian Air
Andante
57.
p
p
mf
mf

Alpine Horn
Andante
HEINRICH PROCH
58.
mf con espressione
mf con espressione
Fine
f
f
cresc.
cresc.
D.S.
The Hermit
Allegro poco Andante
LAMBERT
59.
p
pp

Der Freischütz

(Excerpt)

Poco Andantino

CARL MARIA von WEBER

60.

Waltz: Flower of Damascus

SAVERIO

Waltz

(from *I puritani*)

VINCENZO BELLINI

62.

Prayer

(from *Mosè in Egitto*)

GIOACHINO ROSSINI

Siege of Rochelle

Moderato **MICHAEL WILLIAM BALFE**

64.

Hail! Star of Mary

HEINRICH PROCH

The Two Friends

Martha

(Excerpt)

FRIEDRICH von FLOTOW

Larghetto
p
p
mf
mf
ad lib.
a tempo
ff
ff
The Fox Hunters
Allegro
68.
f
f
pp
ff
ff
rall.

a tempo
Più mosso

IX. Concluding Remarks: 14 Characteristic Studies

The following fourteen studies have been specifically written to provide the student with suitable material with which to test his powers of endurance. In taking up these studies, he will doubtless be fatigued, especially at the outset, by those numbers requiring an unusual length of breath. However, through careful study and experience he will learn to overcome the difficulties and will acquire the resources which will enable him to master this particular phase of playing with ease. As a means to this end, attention is drawn to *cantabile* passages in particular, which should be played with the utmost expression, yet at the same time with as much modified tone as possible. On the cornet, as with the voice, clear tones may be obtained by widening the lips and veiled tones by contracting them. This happy circumstance allows the performer an opportunity to rest while still continuing to play, and at the same time enables him to introduce effective contrasts into the execution. It should be noted that by little artifices of this kind, and by skillfully conserving his resources, the player will reach the end of the longest and most fatiguing pieces, not only without difficulty, but even with a reserve of strength and power, which, when brought to bear on the final measures of a performance, never fails to impress an audience.

The twelve pieces that conclude this book are the embodiment of the various instructions contained in this volume, and they will be found to contain all the articulations, as well as all the difficulties, for which the solutions have already been given. They will also be found to contain melodies calculated to develop the taste of the student, and to render it as complete and as perfect as possible.

At this point my task as professor (using the written instead of the spoken word) will end. There are things which appear clear enough when stated verbally but which when written down on paper cause confusion, seem obscure, and even sometimes appear trivial.

There are other things of such an elevated and subtle nature that neither speech nor word can clearly explain them. They are felt, they are conceived, but they are not to be explained; and yet these things constitute the elevated style, the *grand ecole*, which it is my ambition to establish for the cornet, just as they already exist for singing and for the various kinds of other instruments.

Those of my readers who are ambitious and who want to attain this high level of perfection, should above all things, always try to hear good music well interpreted. They must seek out, among singers and instrumentalists, the most illustrious models, and by doing this purify their taste, develop their sentiments, and bring themselves as near as possible to that which is beautiful. Perhaps then the innate spark which may someday be destined to demonstrate their own talent, will reveal itself and render them worthy of being, in their turn, cited and imitated in the future.

—Jean Baptiste Arban

14 Characteristic Studies

Allegro moderato ♩ = c. 96

1.

mf

mp

Fine

f

f

p

mf

START
f
mf
f
mp
mf
rall.
D.C.
O21X

Use one breath for the first sixteen measures.

Legato ♩ = c. 120

2.

Agitato ♩ = 120
pp
f
rall.
a tempo
pp

Moderato ♩ = c. 86
3.
mp
cresc.
f
dim.
pp
p

p
p
mf
mp
pp
6
cresc.
ff

Allegretto ♩ = c. 88
4.
mf
mp
p
cresc.
f
mp
mf

pp
cresc.
p
cresc.
mf
cresc.
f

Allegro ♩ = c. 104
5.
3
pp
mf
dim.
pp
p
mp

mf
cresc.
f
f
mf
dim.
pp
mf
dim.
dim.
pp
cresc.
f
f

Moderato ♩. = c. 76
6.
mf
p
pp
f

mf
p
pp
cresc.
rall.
dim.
a tempo
mf
p
f
f

Allegro ♩ = c. 76
7.
ff
dim.
pp
rit.
Più mosso
p
mf
p

Più lento
pp
Più agitato
Tempo I
ff

Allegro moderato ♩ = c. 104
8.
mp
simile
p
cresc.
f
dim.
p cantabile
poco rall.
a tempo
mf

rall.
a tempo

Allegro ♩ = c. 124
9.
f
f
mp

rall.
Più largo
p
rall.
Più Allegro
f
mp
mf
f

Allegro ♩ = c. 124

10.

mf

f

cresc.

Più lento
f
p
rall.
D.S.

Allegretto ♩ = c. 96
11.
f
f
pp
Più lento
espress.
mf

mp
p
f
f

Allegro moderato ♩ = c. 100
12.
f
cantabile
p dolce

mp
f
O21X

Allegro non troppo ♩ = c. 96
13.
p

Legato chromatique ♩. = c. 76
14.
p
tr
tr

X. 12 Celebrated Fantaisies and Airs Variés

No. 1: **Fantaisie and Variations** on a Cavatina from *Beatrice di Tenda* by Vincenzo Bellini
No. 2: **Fantaisie and Variations** on *Actéon* by Marc-Antoine Charpentier
No. 3: **Fantaisie Brillante**
No. 4: **Variations on a Tyrolean Song**
No. 5: **Variations on "Vois-tu la neige qui brille"** (The Beautiful Snow)
No. 6: **Cavatina and Variations**
No. 7: **Air Varié** on a Folk Song *The Little Swiss Boy*
No. 8: **Caprice and Variations**
No. 9: **Fantaisie and Variations on a German Theme**
No. 10: **Variations on a Theme by Carl Maria von Weber**
No. 11: **Fantaisie and Variations** on *The Carnival of Venice*
No. 12: **Variations** on a Theme from *Norma* by Vincenzo Bellini

No. 1: Fantaisie and Variations

on a Cavatina
from *Beatrice di Tenda* by Vincenzo Bellini
for Cornet in B♭

JEAN BAPTISTE ARBAN
Revised by Edwin Franko Goldman

Var. I ♩ = c. 100
mf
7
Var. II ♩ = c. 116
mf

7
Var. III and Finale I ♩ = c. 112
Triple tonguing
6
6
6
6
6
mp
p
mp
p
mp
mp
tr
tr
3
3
8

Finale II ♩ = c. 124
mf
tu ku tu ku tu ku
tu ku tu ku tu ku
tr
tr
cresc.
f

No. 2: Fantaisie and Variations

on *Actéon* by Marc-Antoine Charpentier
for Cornet in A

JEAN BAPTISTE ARBAN
Revised by Edwin Franko Goldman

Theme
Allegro
p
tr
Più lento
a tempo
f
veloce
rit.
a tempo
p
tr
ad lib.
16
Var. I
Vivace
3
p
3
Più lento
mf
a tempo
p
cresc.
f
rall.
f
Tempo I
mp

16
Più moderato
mf
rall.
a tempo
tu ku tu tu ku
tu ku tu tu ku
mf
ad lib.
rall.
tu ku tu tu ku
Allegro
16

Finale
Allegro

No. 3: Fantaisie Brillante

for Cornet in B♭

JEAN BAPTISTE ARBAN
Revised by Edwin Franko Goldman

Andantino
Theme
p dolce
mf
poco agitato
a tempo
p
dolce
7
Var. I
3
p
rall.
Tempo I
p

ad lib.
7
Var. II
(Double tonguing may be used ad lib.)
p
rit.
a tempo
7

Var. III
dim.
cresc. ed accel. sin' al fine
ad lib.

No. 4: Variations on a Tyrolean Song

for Cornet in B♭

JEAN BAPTISTE ARBAN
Revised by Edwin Franko Goldman

Var. II
p
mf
p
mf
rall.
a tempo
p
7
Var. III
p
mf

rall.
a tempo
p
7
Var. IV
mf
simile
7

* These four measures may be omitted.

No. 5: Variations on "Vois-tu la neige qui brille"

(The Beautiful Snow)

for Cornet in B♭

JEAN BAPTISTE ARBAN

Revised by Edwin Franko Goldman

Var. II
mf
rit.
a tempo
mf
7
Var. III
p
mp

p
7
Finale
Lento
p
rit.
Allegro
Use double tonguing ad lib.
mf
cresc.
f

No. 6: Cavatina and Variations

for Cornet in B♭

JEAN BAPTISTE ARBAN
Revised by Edwin Franko Goldman

Andante

Piano

p *f* *lento* 7

Theme
Moderato

p *mf* *p* *f* 1. 2. 7

Var. I
sempre stacc.
p
3
1.
2.
7
Var. II
p
rall.
a tempo
mf
1.
2.
7

Var. III
p
3
f
tr
cresc.
f

No. 7: Air Varié

on a Folk Song *The Little Swiss Boy*

for Cornet in B♭

JEAN BAPTISTE ARBAN

Revised by Edwin Franko Goldman

Introduction
Andante

Piano

p

Cadenza ad lib.

Cadenza ad lib.

rall.

accel.

cresc.

a piacere

Cadenza ad lib.

7

Theme
Andante (♪)
p
mf
rall.
a tempo
p
cresc.
rall.
a tempo
7
Var. I
ff
p
f
rall.
a tempo
p
rall.
a tempo
ff
p
f
rall.
a tempo
p
rall.
a tempo
f
p
ff
p
f
rall.
a tempo
p

rall.
a tempo
7
Var. II
mf
p tukutukutuku tukutukutuku
cresc.
(Triple tonguing)
7
Var. III
Adagio
p
mf
6
6
tr

rall.
7
Var. IV et Finale
Allegro
tu tu ku tu tu ku
tu tu ku tu tu ku
rit.
a tempo
cresc.
accel.

No. 8: Caprice and Variations

for Cornet in B♭

JEAN BAPTISTE ARBAN
Revised by Edwin Franko Goldman

Andante moderato ♩ = c. 92
p
rall.
a tempo
p
7
Var. I
Allegro moderato
mf
f

p
cresc.
7
Var. II
p
f
f
p
cresc.
7

Var. III
Più lento
p
ossia:
cresc.
f

No. 9: Fantaisie and Variations
on a German Theme
for Cornet in B♭
JEAN BAPTISTE ARBAN
Revised by Edwin Franko Goldman
Allegro moderato
Piano
Theme
Andante ♩ = c. 86

Var. I
3
p
p
7
Var. II
f
f
p

rit.
a tempo
f
f
7
Var. III
mf
6
6
6
3
3
3
3
7

Finale
mf
mp
f
ff
tr

No. 10: Variations on a Theme by Carl Maria von Weber

for Cornet in B♭

JEAN BAPTISTE ARBAN

Revised by Edwin Franko Goldman

Theme
Andante non troppo
p
mf
rall.
a tempo
p
rall.
7
Var. I
p
p
p
rall.
a tempo
p
7
Var. II
p

rall.
a tempo
7
Var. III
Più lento
poco a poco cresc.
rall.
a tempo
15

Var. IV
6
6
3
3
pp
pp
f
p
f
p
pp
cresc.
tu tu ku tu tu tu tu
ff

No. 11: Fantaisie and Variations

on *The Carnival of Venice*

for Cornet in B♭

JEAN BAPTISTE ARBAN

Revised by Edwin Franko Goldman

Var. I (♪)
Double tonguing
p
ff
f

7
Var. II
Poco più mosso
p
7

Var. III
Andante (♪)
p
pp
tu ku
tu ku
tu ku
tu ku

7
Var. IV (♪)
mf
Coda
f
tu ku tu ku tu ku
tu tu ku tu tu tu tu

No. 12: Variations

on a Theme from *Norma* by Vincenzo Bellini
for Cornet in B♭

JEAN BAPTISTE ARBAN
Revised by Edwin Franko Goldman

cresc.
f
7
Var. I
p
mf
f
cresc.
cresc.
f
p
f
7

Var. II
6
6
6
6
p
p
pp